An Excellent Report Card for Geography Teachers

The good news is coming in from all over the United States: Geography is making a comeback.

David Geyer, geography teacher at Penn High School in Mishawaka, Indiana, tells us that during the past two years, enrollment in geography classes at his school has jumped from 60 to 350 students.

"We had to add 14 classes to meet the demand," says David, a 1988 graduate of the Society's Summer Geography Institute.

In Colorado Springs, Colorado, social studies coordinator Kathryn Lapp reports that the number of world geography classes being offered to high school seniors has rocketed from 5 to 29.

Schools in Frederick County, Maryland, this fall will offer geography as a separate course for the first time in 20 years, says Sari Bennett, a geography professor at [...] sity of Maryland, Balti[...]

A great deal of credit [...] renaissance belongs to t[...] graphic Alliance Networ[...] tion of grass roots organi[...] bringing together academic geographers, teachers from many disciplines, and others dedicated to improving geography instruction.

These extraordinary volunteer educators have responded to the alliance initiated by the National Geographic Society. Now active in 40 states and Puerto Rico, alliances sponsor geography workshops for teachers, develop classroom materials, lead public-awareness activities, and work with local, state, and national leaders to reform curricula.

Training programs have reached tens of thousands of teachers. "It has changed my professional life, my department's activities, and the teaching methods of many teachers," says Michael Libbee, a geography professor at Central Michigan University and a coordinator of the Michigan Geographic Alliance.

Patricia Hardy, a high school

[...] the Texas [...] inted to the [...] nomic Policy [...] is to establish [...] icy Center. She [...] an excellent position to apply the advocacy skills she learned at the National Geographic Instructional Leadership Institute in 1989.

Begun in 1986 with seven alliances in six states, the network now boasts an active membership of some 63,000 people—all working together to show that geography is an important tool for responsible citizenship, environmental awareness, and political understanding.

We at the Society have always believed that teachers are the key to revitalizing geography, and our support for them has been richly rewarded. We will continue to assist the alliances as they keep growing, but they must also have the continued support of members and friends. The return to our nation is certainly worth the investment.

Gilbert M. Grosvenor

States taking part in the Geographic Alliance Network are shown in red. The latest additions are Iowa, Kansas, Nevada, North Dakota, Rhode Island, and Wyoming, along with Puerto Rico. Can you locate them?

THE NATIONAL GEOGRAPHIC SOCIETY EDUCATION FOUNDATION WAS ESTABLISHED IN 1988 TO HELP RAISE AND DISTRIBUTE FUNDS FOR EDUCATIONAL AND SCIENTIFIC PROGRAMS.

Forum

Russia on a New Course

In the February 1991 article about Mother Russia, Mike Edwards hit the nail on the head when he told that the Solovetskiy Monastery is "Russia in a capsule." In the yard is a church bell used on the island of Manamansalo in Finland's Lake Oulujärvi a few hundred years ago. The Russians "borrowed" it, along with some pieces of Finland later on. Since the bell lies unused, how about returning it and building a new church together? We could find the timber, nails, and paint, if the Russians would provide the bell and a few carpenters. Then we would believe that Russia is on a new course.

RISTO O. MAJANIEMI
Kuhmo, Finland

You refer to Lenin as Vladimir Ilyich Lenin. I do not dispute that that is how the first secretary general of the Soviet Union is best known, but his surname is Ulyanov. He acquired the sobriquet Lenin due to his lengthy period of incarceration in a fortress located on the Lena River.

GUI SOUZA-LEITE
St. Catharines, Ontario

In the photograph of teens in Volgograd (page 33), one's amazement that a $12 souvenir T-shirt from the Clam Hut in Highlands, New Jersey, could be considered chic in Volgograd is surpassed only by wonderment about how it got there.

ALFRED J. WEISS
Dunellen, New Jersey

Three Russians from Volgograd on a Bridges for Peace program visited the Clam Hut last year.

It may be deduced from the ribbons worn by the irate Russian tank colonel (pages 3-4) that he served at least 30 years in the Red Army, holds three gallantry decorations, and took part in the battles for Königsberg and Berlin in World War II. While his bellicose attitude toward Russian liberals may be regrettable, it is understandable.

EAMONN O'TOOLE
Limerick, Ireland

The Time Tapestry (pages 5-8) should have included that between 1914 and 1918 Russia was totally involved in World War I. Through the peace treaty of Brest-Litovsk it lost not only Polish territories and the Baltic provinces but also Finland and Ukraine. The events were cataclysmic for Russia;
they contributed to the end of the tsars, to the civil war, and to the beginning of the Soviet system.

TINO AHRENS
Stone Mountain, Georgia

California's Central Valley

"Harvest of Change" suggests that the California Department of Health Services does not believe that child cancer rates are elevated in McFarland. In fact since 1985 CDHS has recognized that a child cancer cluster exists there. What we reported at the May 18, 1990, meeting was that overall child cancer rates *in the four counties* surrounding McFarland were not unusual when compared with rates elsewhere in the United States. Urban nonagricultural areas had the highest rates, while rural nonagricultural areas had the lowest. Unfortunately, it is very difficult to find causes of cancer, especially when the absolute number of cases is low and there is no obvious contaminant.

LYNN R. GOLDMAN, M.D.
Department of Health Services
Berkeley, California

The comparison of a "natural" farm to a "sterile," chemically dependent one is misleading. As an eastern fruit grower, I have long used pesticides. During the growing season there are birds nesting in the trees and bees and butterflies visiting the wildflowers on the orchard floor. Many chemical pesticides are specific to the target pest and break down quickly. It is a mistake to assume that all man-made chemicals are harmful to the environment and all organic, or "natural," ones are safe.

DANA M. SULIN
Fitchburg, Massachusetts

A key to the development of California—water—was not presented with the correct impartiality. It is disappointing that you did not speak with more farmers. Water can cost a mere $3.50 an acre-foot but is often 10 to 30 times that amount. Likewise there isn't a single farmer who wishes that it not rain; he hopes for every drop he can get. Before the Central Valley Project the valley was inhospitable and unproductive. The desert and swamps were transformed into productive agricultural land at a cost borne not by U. S. taxpayers but by farmers and communities in the area that put up their own farmland as collateral for this project.

MARC W. COOL
Bakersfield, California

I live in the Sierra Nevada, where water is collected for use by farmers in the Central Valley. With cheap, subsidized federal water they grow tropical fruits and high-water-use crops such as, of all things, rice. In the meantime, my family is required to cut back on our water consumption by 40 percent. Our two county reservoirs will run out of water about mid-May, while there is still water available in federal reservoirs for growing rice in the desert. What is wrong with this picture?

WAYNE E. CHRISTENSEN
Sonora, California

Since we received Mr. Christensen's letter, the crisis has been alleviated. Snowmelt from the mountains has filled the two county reservoirs.

Surma of Ethiopia

This superb piece showed the incredible pride that the Surma people rightfully feel about their ethnicity. It highlighted the unique customs without making the Surma seem bizarre or inferior.

LAURA L. MITIC
Ellicott City, Maryland

Are we supposed to admire this culture that so terribly mutilates its women? Are any of the men so deliberately deformed? This is 1991, not 1891.

MALLORY D. HART
New York, New York

The use of lip plates was quite common among women in the east-central African interior during the 19th century. People of northern Mozambique explained that the disfigurement caused by the plates made their women unappealing to slave traders from the Indian Ocean coast. The fact that use of the plates ceased in east-central Africa after the slave trade ended gives substantial credence to this explanation. By extension, it raises the question as to the duration of the slave trade in the southern Ethiopian area.

LEROY VAIL
History Department, Harvard University
Cambridge, Massachusetts

Hong Kong

It is about time that people realize the terror that Hong Kong people will face in 1997. As a Hong Kong citizen, I am happy to know that whatever may happen when China takes control, memories of this dazzling city will still exist in this issue.

VINCENT TAM
Irvine, California

An impression was left that may dissuade people from visiting the crown colony on the basis of expense: $1,000 for three days, as suggested by a money changer. We recently spent ten days in Hong Kong; our hotel was $50 (Canadian) per night per person. Allowing $25 for meals permits eating in reasonably good establishments. The marvelous transportation network and Star Ferry are inexpensive. We recommend the practical brochures from the Hong Kong Tourist Association.

KEN WOOLLEY
Scarborough, Ontario

Britain does not have a lease on all of Hong Kong. In the Convention of Peking in 1898 the New Territories from the China border to Boundary Street in Kowloon was leased. The remaining parts of Kowloon, the harbor, and Hong Kong Island were ceded to Great Britain.

Most Hong Kong Chinese I know would greet the figure of $11,500 per capita income with open-mouthed awe. It is inflated by individuals who have millions of dollars in income. I think a median income of $4,000 to $5,000 might be closer.

One hopes the new owners will be sensitive to the needs of these fine, hardworking people.

ROBERT FOY
Kirkland, Washington

Middle East Map

I am a U. S. Marine currently [February] stationed near the front lines in Operation Desert Storm. My squadron mates and I especially enjoyed the Middle East map, which we used as a training aid.

SGT. JOSEPH UNWIN
FPO San Francisco, California

The hostilities were only five days old when your map arrived. It recalls the early days of World War II when we had a NATIONAL GEOGRAPHIC map of the Asian-Pacific area, one of the best available at the time.

KENNETH RIVOIRE
Pawling, New York

About 200 miles north of Jiddah, Saudi Arabia, you show the old Arab seaport of Yanbu al Bahr, but not the modern town of Yanbu as Sinaiyah, six miles to the southeast. Extending 15 miles along the Red Sea coastline, its oil refineries, petrochemical complexes, industrial plants, and a strategic port facility support a residential community of 25,000. It is here that the terminals of the crude oil and gas pipelines are located, rather than within the Yanbu al Bahr area, as shown.

ADAM S. BERESTYNSKI
Laguna Beach, California

It is evident that the population figures you quoted for Saudi Arabia, Kuwait, and the other Gulf States were furnished by the governments concerned. Be aware that those figures include an often substantial foreign work force.

NAZAR AL-AMIR
Pampigny, Switzerland

Thank you for your continued support of the education system and the professionals who strive to make it successful. Your insert map has been put to use to answer questions, allay fears, and assist in the writing of current events/research projects.

DOROTHY KELLINGTON
Public School 113, Queens
Glendale, New York

....

Letters should be addressed to FORUM, National Geographic Magazine, Box 37448, Washington, D. C. 20013, and should include sender's address and telephone number. Not all letters can be used. Those that are will often be edited and excerpted.

Geographica

FRED WARD, BLACK STAR

A National Sanctuary for the Florida Keys

The future of Florida's imperiled coral reefs (NATIONAL GEOGRAPHIC, July 1990) may be brighter with the creation of the nation's largest marine sanctuary.

The Florida Keys National Marine Sanctuary has been designed to protect the reefs as well as 2,600 square nautical miles of water embracing both sides of the island chain. The preserve includes the existing Key Largo and Looe Key federal sanctuaries and John Pennekamp Coral Reef State Park.

Established by Congress last fall, the sanctuary is off-limits to most tankers and other large vessels and cannot be mined for seabed minerals. These measures will help improve the water quality and aid the survival of coral reefs and marine wildlife. Equally important, the law calls for a review of land-based pollution, such as septic tank discharge.

The National Oceanic and Atmospheric Administration is to devise a management plan for the sanctuary by May 1993, with help from the Environmental Protection Agency and the state of Florida. Workshops beginning this month will solicit public comment. Timothy R. E. Keeney, the former NOAA official who helped plan the federal effort, calls it a chance "to get a handle on the health" of the marine environment and preserve it. Bill Mott of the Center for Marine Conservation, a national environmental group, terms the law a "turning point" because it allows an attack on land-based pollution but emphasizes it will take millions of dollars to run the sanctuary's research, education, and enforcement programs.

Soldiers as Artists: World War II Murals

There are scantily clad women, and knights and minstrels. There are circus clowns and B-17 bombers, mermaids and sailors, and a warning over a door that reads: "Abandon hope, all ye who enter here."

Members of the U. S. Eighth Army Air Force stationed in England between 1942 and 1945 (GEOGRAPHIC, March 1945) left their mark on the walls of barracks and officers' and enlisted men's clubs at more than 120 hastily constructed airfields in East Anglia. Between bombing runs and dogfights with German fighters, they painted their dreams and their nightmares. The murals offer insight into the minds of American men at war far from home.

Dave Lande of Appleton, Wisconsin, learned of the artwork as he researched a book on the Eighth Air Force, the first air combat unit to arrive in force in the European theater. By the end of World War II the Eighth deployed 200,000 airmen; more than 300,000 had passed through it.

Many of the buildings the airmen decorated have crumbled or have been torn down. But a surprising number remain almost half a century later.

"There are no graffiti on the paintings, which amazed me," Lande says. Britons have such affection for the art that a group called the Eighth War Art Conservation Society preserves whole sections of painted walls from buildings they learn are to be razed.

ANDREW MORLAND

Geographica

NGS PHOTOGRAPHER VICTOR R. BOSWELL, JR.

Luxury Cast-offs for Mount Vernon Slaves?

The chief archaeologist at George Washington's Mount Vernon was surprised as he studied the artifacts he and his team had dug up. "Most of what we found I would expect to find around a planter's house," he said.

But Dennis J. Pogue and his team had been excavating a six-foot-square trash-filled cellar beneath the quarters of the house slaves at Washington's Virginia mansion.

"They were still victims of a dehumanizing institution," Pogue says, but the high quality of the ceramic sherds—including some of imported Chinese porcelain—and the buckles, buttons, and fragments of glasses and wine bottles suggest that these slaves lived better, in a material sense, than might be expected.

More evidence comes from the animal bones found in the slaves' trash. It suggests they could trap, fish, even hunt to give themselves a better, more diverse diet than most slaves are believed to have received. The 60 or so slaves who lived in these quarters a few hundred yards from the mansion were weavers and spinners, house servants and blacksmiths. Whether slaves who toiled in Washington's outlying tobacco fields lived as well is not known.

As for the ceramics, Pogue thinks that George and Martha Washington passed them on when they became chipped, cracked, or merely unfashionable.

U. S. Tick Collection Finds a New Home

The U. S. government has solved the problem of who should pay for the upkeep on a million dead ticks by sending them to Georgia.

The National Institutes of Health has shipped the National Tick Collection to Georgia Southern University in Statesboro with a five-year, million-dollar grant to maintain it. The Smithsonian had held the collection since 1983 but could no longer store it. Curator James Keirans (below), who accompanied the collection to Georgia, is one of the world's top experts in identifying

NICK ARROYO

ticks, which carry such infectious diseases as Rocky Mountain spotted fever and Lyme disease (GEOGRAPHIC, January 1991). The university will support the collection when the grant expires.

The collection—by far the world's largest, with specimens from 760 of the 850 known species—is a vital tool in determining if a tick could be carrying disease. "I'm talking about an animal that can transmit diseases that can kill you," Dr. Keirans says.

Unexpected Study Yields Data on Mystery Cat

Warren Johnson and William Franklin didn't plan to study the habits of the wild Geoffroy's cat. But when several of the elusive felines were captured as the Iowa State University scientists tracked Patagonia pumas (GEOGRAPHIC, January 1991)—well, says Johnson, "It would have been a crime to throw away the data."

Geoffroy's cat, named for French naturalist Geoffroy St. Hilaire, is a spotted feline about two feet long, found from southern Brazil and Bolivia to the tip of South America. Its pelt has been the world's most commonly traded cat pelt: Argentina alone exported some 450,000 skins from 1976 to 1980. But despite its familiarity to local trappers, scientists knew nothing of the cat's behavior.

GAIL BLUNDELL

Johnson, Franklin, and their team captured nine cats, fitted them with ear tags and radio collars, and set them free. They found that the cats, especially males, are generally loners; that they roam areas with dense vegetation at night; and that their prime prey are European hares, especially during the spring and summer, when the hares produce their young.

Geographica

RICHARD THOMPSON

If Today Is Tuesday, Where Is New Mexico?

No wonder New Mexico's license tags now say "New Mexico, U.S.A." New Mexico became a United States territory in 1846, a state in 1912. But many people seem to have trouble understanding that and misplace it, usually south of the border in what might be called Old Mexico. Since 1970 *New Mexico Magazine*—published by the state's tourism department—has collected tales of confusion in a good-natured column called "One of Our Fifty is Missing." Examples:

"If it's Friday in Texas, will it be Friday in New Mexico?" a Texan asked. A Santa Fe woman was told that Medicare did not cover services outside the U. S. An Indiana church camp flew flags of 30 nations where the church had missionaries—and included New Mexico's among them. A New Mexico native was told by a California woman, "You speak English so well!" An Illinois woman called an airline about Albuquerque flight information and was connected to the international desk. A Midwest school sent a New Mexico student a form to "expedite your entry into the United States."

Emily Drabanski, the magazine's editor in chief, says the column is a reader favorite. She has her own tale: A San Francisco cab driver who learned she was from landlocked New Mexico recently told her, "The beaches are lovely there."

Social-Climbing Moms in the Monkey World

Monkeys are physical climbers. And, it seems, they are social climbers too. Primatologist Frans B. M. de Waal was studying female rhesus monkeys at the Wisconsin Regional Primate Center in Madison when he noticed an unusual and previously undocumented pattern of behavior: A monkey mother holding her infant would pick up and also hold a wandering second infant for periods ranging from a few seconds to ten minutes in length.

De Waal began to compile statistics on the frequency of what he calls "double-holds" and now believes that the mother was trying to choose her baby's friends. In more than 90 percent of the cases the mother would pick up an infant from a family that ranked higher than hers in the monkey group's social structure.

"We believe that the purpose is to try to see their offspring play with

Suggestions for GEOGRAPHICA may be submitted to Boris Weintraub, NATIONAL GEOGRAPHIC, Box 37357, Washington, D. C. 20036, and should include the sender's address and telephone number.

FRANS B. M. DE WAAL

peers from high-ranking families rather than low-ranking ones," de Waal says. And the sense of purpose is strong: In several cases, de Waal and his researchers saw a mother spot an infant from a higher-ranking family, rush off to pick up her own infant, then dash back to pick up the other for a double-hold.

"It's an interesting human parallel," de Waal notes drily. He plans to keep an eye on the monkeys as they mature to see if the bonds of friendship endure.

Examining 500 Years of Spanish Presence

Since the time California was ceded to the United States, a ranch has existed on Santa Rosa Island, one of the Channel Islands off Santa Barbara (GEOGRAPHIC, August 1958). Next summer, visitors to the island—now part of Channel Islands National Park—will have a chance to see the descendants of Spanish settlers, Mexican cowboys called *vaqueros,* herd cattle, shoe horses, and live the traditional vaquero life.

The Island Vaquero Festival will be one of many ways the National Park Service will mark the 500th anniversary of the arrival of the Spanish in the New World. The Park Service has named 38 of its parks, historic sites, monuments, and memorials Spanish Colonial Heritage Sites and has asked each to prepare programs that focus on the cultural exchange between Spaniards and Native Americans. The sites range from Alaska's Sitka National Historical Park, an area explored by a Spanish expedition in 1775, to De Soto National Memorial in Tampa Bay, Florida, where the explorer is believed to have landed in 1539.

INTRODUCE A FRIEND
TO THE WONDERS
OF NATIONAL GEOGRAPHIC!

Treat a friend to countless fascinations every month with a gift membership in the National Geographic Society. You can be sure your friend will thank you for sharing the wonders of NATIONAL GEOGRAPHIC. Mail your check with this form today to start your gift membership.

☐ National Geographic Society
Washington, D.C. 20036 U.S.A.
Copyright © 1991 National Geographic Society

JUST $21*
for 12 months
July 1991-June 1992

☐ Enclosed is my check for a gift membership for the person named below.

☐ I have enclosed *my* membership dues.

MY NAME:
_____
(Print full name of an individual only: Mr., Mrs., Miss, Ms.)

_____
Street

_____
City, State/Province

_____
Country, Zip/Postal Code

GIFT FOR:
_____
Name (Print full name of an individual only: Mr., Mrs., Miss, Ms.)

_____
Street

_____
City, State/Province

_____
Country, Zip/Postal Code   00691

Gift card
should read: *From* _____

Mail to: National Geographic Society, P.O. Box 2895
Washington, D.C. 20013 U.S.A.

*U.S. rate; for Canada remit $30.45 U.S. funds ($36.50 Canadian funds), which includes 7% GST. For all other countries, $31.30 U.S. funds, payable by bank draft in U.S. funds on a U.S. bank or by international money order in U.S. funds. *Please add 5% sales tax for memberships being sent to any Maryland address.* Eighty percent of dues is designated for subscription to the magazine. Membership begins with July 1991 issue.
Life membership (U.S. addresses only): $550.

NATIONAL
GEOGRAPHIC

JUNE 1991

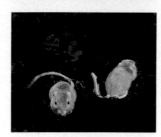

COVER: Carbon-blackened boys play near a factory in Copşa Mică, Romania, in the heart of polluted Eastern Europe. Photograph by James Nachtwey.

FOR MEMBERSHIP INFORMATION CALL 1-800-638-4077

AGE-OLD CHALLENGE:

The wasteful use of water resources may be

By BRUCE BABBITT

ACH NIGHT as the sun goes down and the desert darkens, the neon lights of Las Vegas, Nevada, flare into the sky. Beneath the lurid glow of giant casino signs, water splashes in Roman fountains, runs into acres of swimming pools, and overflows into street gutters.

Las Vegas, prodigal playground of the West, illustrates the conflict between man and nature in the Colorado River basin. Within just ten years the metropolitan area could be using virtually every drop of Nevada's legal share of the Colorado River's flow. City leaders, expecting the population of 800,000 to double in the next 40 years, are searching far and wide for new water supplies.

City water engineers are advocating a traditional solution: an engineering project to tap into the underground waters beneath remote valleys of eastern Nevada. They propose a system of 145 huge wells spread across nearly 20 percent of the state and connected by a thousand miles of pipeline. Cost estimates range

The author, a former governor of Arizona, is an attorney who specializes in representing rural interests in water-rights disputes.

from 1.5 billion to four billion dollars.

Environmental costs may be as high or higher, if less easy to quantify. Critics contend that groundwater pumping will lower the water table, destroying streams and marshes that sustain migratory waterfowl and nourish plant and wildlife oases in desert basins, including distant Death Valley National Monument in California. Even there, in the hottest desert in North America, water lies beneath the ground. Fearful for the future, the National Park Service has filed formal protests against the project.

Water reformers throughout the West are beginning to question these expensive, environmentally damaging water-transfer projects. They insist that there is a better way. If westerners would strongly promote conservation and develop plans to recycle and reuse existing water supplies, there would be no immediate need for more such projects.

Reformers point to Tucson, Arizona, as a good example of a desert city that today supports growth by conserving and reusing water. More and more streets and parks are planted with the trees and flowering plants of the surrounding

WATER AND THE WEST

how the West is lost.

Sonoran Desert. Residents receive free pamphlets explaining xeriscaping, the art of landscaping with low-water-use plants. City ordinances require low-flow toilets, shower heads, and faucets, and the city has even shared the cost of more efficient toilets for older homes. Many golf courses and parks are watered with treated sewage effluent.

Tucson residents are proud of their distinctive "desert city" image. The payoff is clear: On a per capita basis, Tucson now consumes about half the water of Las Vegas, where conservation is still voluntary.

As the following article makes starkly clear, communities dependent on the Colorado River are facing a crisis. The river is being used to the fullest, and the region is now in its fifth year of drought.

As urban populations continue to grow, the battle between the traditional water engineers, known in the West as "water buffaloes," and the emerging reform movement will surely intensify. The question, as yet unanswered, is whether man can live and prosper with nature, respecting the limits of our desert environment.

JIM RICHARDSON

Water erupts from a mock volcano at the Mirage Hotel in Las Vegas. In the West, demand for water exceeds supply, so this hotel uses mostly waste-water to create its lavish desert magic.

THE COLORADO

A River Drained Dry

By JIM CARRIER

Photographs by JIM RICHARDSON WEST LIGHT

T
HE MAN THEY CALL El Coyote pushed his blue dinghy away from the bulrushes, stroked through the murky brown residue of the Colorado River, and began to pull up his gill net. Halfway through pulling in the 130-foot net, he found an eight-inch mullet that landed with a lonely plunk in an orange pail at his feet. Minutes passed before I heard the plastic thud again, and by the time the whole net lay empty in the boat, there were just three fish in his bucket.

"At least it's breakfast," Ricardo Sandoval said to me. "The net's been out here two days." El Coyote, so nicknamed for his days as a crafty baseball player, paddled back home to El Mayor, the ramshackle settlement of the Cucapá Indians, the "river people" who are last in line for the waters of the Colorado River system (map, pages 16-17).

Fifty miles south of the U. S. border in Mexico's Baja California, the great river of the West that I had followed from beginning to end was gone, the water in its bed a shallow, narrow sump of salt and pesticide-laced runoff from crop irrigation.

"*Es nuestra vida*—It is our life," said El Coyote, summing up 2,000 years of his

people's sustenance from this area. But for half a century the delta had been dying, and with it the Cucapá culture. No longer can tribal members hunt mule deer, plant squash with the floods, harvest wild salt grass, or eat fish three times a day. Several species of fish and plant life have disappeared. The settlement has shrunk to about 85 families. The once rich estuary is filled with weeds, trash, and occasional swamps of unhealthy water—barely enough to float their boats. Last year, the fourth year of drought, the water dropped to its lowest level in tribal memory. The Cucapá were lucky to eat fish once a week.

"We are the river people. We're still here," said Ricardo. "But what river? I haven't seen it. It doesn't get this far."

While most mapmakers draw a vibrant blue line from the central Rocky Mountains to the Gulf of California, the nets of the Cucapá tell a poignant truth about the Colorado River: (Continued on page 10)

Dories beached at dawn in the Grand Canyon will soon plunge through rapids on a once wild river so dammed and diverted that it vanishes before reaching its old outlet to the sea.

Western-style watering hole: Labor Day boaters pack Copper Canyon in Lake Havasu on the Arizona-California border. Impounded by Parker Dam, this 45-mile-long lake sends a billion gallons of water a day barreling through the

Colorado River Aqueduct, a 242-mile-long lifeline to southern California cities. While dams provide flood control, hydroelectric power, water storage, and recreation, they drown canyons, alter ecosystems, and threaten native species.

The Colorado: A River Drained Dry

*Umbilical of water zigzags through hilly, saguaro cactus country northwest of
Phoenix. When completed, this 3.5-billion-dollar Bureau of Reclamation
network of aqueducts, called the Central Arizona Project, will bring nearly half*

a trillion gallons of Colorado River water a year 335 miles from Lake Havasu to central Arizona farms, Indian reservations, industries, and fast-growing municipalities. End-of-the-line Tucson will drink its first drop in 1992.

The Colorado: A River Drained Dry

(Continued from page 4) Demand has finally exceeded the river's capacity to support the Southwest.

For a river bigger than life such a condition seems unthinkable. Plunging from frozen heights of 14,000 feet on the continental spine, the Colorado writhes for 1,450 miles. It etches the Rocky Mountains, it carves the

JIM CARRIER is a columnist for the *Denver Post* who often writes on western water issues. Freelance photographer JIM RICHARDSON, also a veteran of the *Denver Post,* covered Atlanta for the July 1988 NATIONAL GEOGRAPHIC.

mile-deep Grand Canyon. For only 56 years have its red-mud floods been under control.

European explorers thought the land it flowed through was useless. "Ours has been the first and will doubtless be the last party of whites to visit this profitless locality," wrote Lt. Joseph C. Ives of the Army Engineers in 1858, after steaming upriver to the present site of Hoover Dam in search of a navigable route between the Rockies and the Pacific. "The Colorado River, along the greater portion of its lonely and majestic way, shall be forever unvisited and undisturbed."

As rivers are measured, the Colorado has only a few superlatives: Its elevational drop is the greatest in North America; it is one of the siltiest (before the dams, it carried an average load of 380,000 tons a day); and it is one of the saltiest, carrying nine million tons a year. Although it ranks seventh in length in the U. S., its water volume has averaged only 15 million acre-feet of water yearly since 1905. (The Columbia empties 192 million and the Mississippi more than 400 million.)

The Colorado system binds the Southwest in a semiarid 244,000-square-mile drainage

Bringing up the rear, Juan Garcia drives his goats along Mexico's Canal Central, the Colorado's last major diversion. Squatters like Garcia line the canal, eking out a living as farmers and field hands.

(an area larger than France) and divides the region as no other element: state against state, rural against urban, Indian against white. It has earned the reputation as the most legislated, litigated, and debated river in the world.

In two years of tracing the Colorado I was

The Colorado: A River Drained Dry

11

stunned by the magnitude of what it was asked to do. The Colorado grows grapes in New Mexico, brews beer in Colorado, raises minnows in Utah, floats rafts in Arizona, lights jackpots in Nevada, nurses elk in Wyoming, freezes ice for California, sweetens cantaloupes in Mexico. In bringing life to 21 million people and more than two million acres of farmland in seven states and two countries, the river has reached a dammed and diverted denouement.

There is only so much water, and demands are increasing. Conflicts are constant among water users. The 1922 Colorado River Compact that divides its waters into two basins for use by seven bordering states—Wyoming, Utah, Colorado, New Mexico, Arizona, Nevada, and California—no longer seems adequate as Americans flood the Sunbelt. New rules must be written in a time of environmental concern and heightened awareness of Native American rights and claims. A new strategy is needed for western water. As the Colorado River nears the end of a fruitful century in which it was harnessed to human needs, it enters an era of limits.

"T HESE GLACIERS really did a number on this country," said John Barlow, a rock-and-roll lyricist and former Wyoming rancher, as we looked out the window of a small plane, nearly touching the gouged granite of Gannett Peak. Sunrise had just topped Wyoming's Wind River Range, one of the Colorado's main sources, and down in the shadows I could see stretch marks on Mammoth Glacier as it slowly ebbed into the Green River, the most northern reach of the Colorado system.

"You could say that the Green was the central river in settling the West," said Barlow. It was the heart of the beaver trade, and John Wesley Powell began his historic exploration of the Colorado in 1869 at the town of Green River in the Wyoming Territory.

Unlike most other Colorado tributaries, which are diverted at their headwaters, the Green has wild beginnings. I could see a moose and her calf clomping at the edge of Upper Green River Lake, a brilliant

Holding back the flow, 726-foot-high Hoover Dam, in operation since 1935, domesticated the Colorado, whose floods once tore through the countryside.

At the Central Arizona Project's computerized control room in Phoenix (below), water is just a keystroke away.

turquoise reflected from glacial silt. Two miles more and the river leaves the wilderness, weaving its way through a sage plain. This is where its virginity ends: Here the first irrigation ditches cut into its banks.

Over a ridge, on the New Fork of the Green, John Barlow's grandfather, Perry W. Jenkins, built his ranch in 1905. He organized Sublette County around the Green's watershed and later helped represent Wyoming in negotiations for the historic 1922 Colorado River Compact. Each summer John flood-irrigated 2,200 acres to grow grass for 1,100 cows. But he lost the ranch to high debt and low beef prices in the late 1980s. The new, absentee owners sold the cattle, and the unused water slipped into the Green, where almost 60 percent of Wyoming's compact share goes for lack of use.

"I would like my kids' kids to live here," said John, who makes a living writing songs for the Grateful Dead. "I don't think the national interest is served by running all the water to where it cleans off driveways in Los Angeles. But I think the compact will be abrogated, and Wyoming will be the loser. This is heretical, but I don't know how we can justify our need for the water under present circumstances."

Three hundred miles to the southeast in

Patchwork in Fraser Experimental Forest near Denver increases spring runoff by letting snow fall on clearings, where it becomes snowpack, instead of on trees, where much evaporates. Water comes under lock and key at a headgate of the Williams Fork River, where Jim Taussig (below) diverts water to his ranch. In 1963 Denver bought the Taussigs' water rights but gave them a 40-year lease. In 2003, their land may be left high and dry.

Colorado, along the Continental Divide, the 12,000-foot Never Summer Mountains have beautiful names: Cumulus, Nimbus, Stratus. With the heart of a poet and big snowshoes, I'd hoped to find one of the river's sources near Lake of the Clouds in Rocky Mountain National Park, which lies below these peaks. The birth here is difficult: The runoff of the serrated mountains is interrupted by a big gouge 14 miles across the mountain breasts. This Grand Ditch runs water eastward across the divide at 10,186 feet, then sends it down the east face of the Rockies to Fort Collins

and 30,000 acres of sugar beets, corn, and barley on the Great Plains.

"Some people thought it was awful to tear up the side of the mountain," said Harvey Johnson, 95, chairman of Water Supply and Storage Company, which owns the water in the ditch. "I tell them we're growing food, and they'd go hungry without it."

First dug by Asian laborers, the ditch carried water by 1900. "We were quite desperate, and the Western Slope was flush with water," Johnson told me. "The company decided they'd just go get it." That was both

14

Making the most of drought, Frank Norton visits the site of his family's former dude ranch, normally covered by Lake Granby. Filled in 1952, this man-made lake is a catchment basin for a major diversion of the Colorado's headwaters, a 13-mile-long tunnel through the Rockies that brings water to farms and cities like Boulder. The Nortons resettled up the hill and built a marina (background).

Plumbing the West

"WE HAVE in the Colorado an American Nile awaiting regulation," said Los Angeles water investigator Joseph B. Lippincott in 1912. Since that time the river has been "regulated" almost out of existence and now rarely empties into the Gulf of California. With scores of reservoirs and diversion dams, hundreds of miles of aqueducts and tunnels, dozens of pumping stations, thousands of miles of canals, and more than 30 hydroelectric plants, the river basin contains one of the world's most controlled river systems.

Riverwide regulation began with the 1922 Colorado River Compact, which divided seven western states into upper and lower basins (map) and allocated 7.5 million acre-feet of water a year to each. A 1944 treaty with Mexico guaranteed that country 1.5 million acre-feet annually. Although the Colorado was committed to deliver 16.5 million acre-feet, its annual flow has averaged only 14 million since 1930, and evaporation from reservoirs removes another 2 million.

As long as some states continue to use less than their share (inset), others can siphon off more. But as populations rise and states in both basins complete water projects, the Colorado will be virtually tapped out.

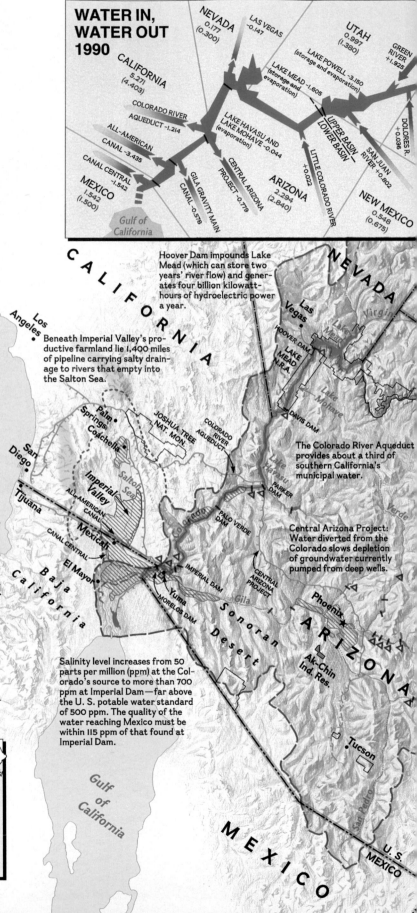

WATER IN, WATER OUT 1990

NEVADA 0.177 (0.300)
LAS VEGAS -0.147
UTAH 0.997 (1.380)
GREEN RIVER +1.925
CALIFORNIA 5.271 (4.403)
LAKE POWELL -3.150 (storage and evaporation)
LAKE MEAD -1.605 (storage and evaporation)
DOLORES R. +0.036
COLORADO RIVER AQUEDUCT -1.214
LAKE HAVASU AND LAKE MOHAVE -0.044 (evaporation)
UPPER BASIN LOWER BASIN
SAN JUAN RIVER +0.802
ALL-AMERICAN CANAL -3.435
LITTLE COLORADO RIVER +0.022
CANAL CENTRAL -1.542
GILA GRAVITY MAIN CANAL -0.578
CENTRAL ARIZONA PROJECT -0.779
ARIZONA 2.294 (2.840)
NEW MEXICO 0.548 (0.675)
MEXICO 1.542 (1.500)
Gulf of California

Hoover Dam impounds Lake Mead (which can store two years' river flow) and generates four billion kilowatt-hours of hydroelectric power a year.

Beneath Imperial Valley's productive farmland lie 1,400 miles of pipeline carrying salty drainage to rivers that empty into the Salton Sea.

The Colorado River Aqueduct provides about a third of southern California's municipal water.

Central Arizona Project: Water diverted from the Colorado slows depletion of groundwater currently pumped from deep wells.

Salinity level increases from 50 parts per million (ppm) at the Colorado's source to more than 700 ppm at Imperial Dam—far above the U. S. potable water standard of 500 ppm. The quality of the water reaching Mexico must be within 115 ppm of that found at Imperial Dam.

CANADA
UNITED STATES
Columbia R.
Sacramento R.
COLORADO RIVER BASIN
Mississippi
MEXICO

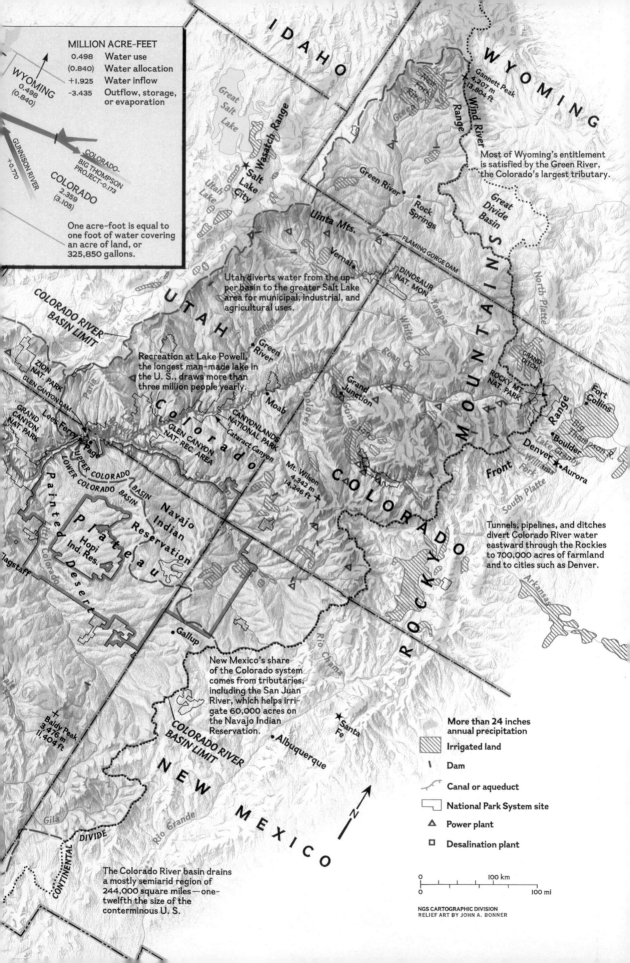

IDAHO

WYOMING

MILLION ACRE-FEET
0.498   Water use
(0.840)   Water allocation
+1.925   Water inflow
-3.435   Outflow, storage, or evaporation

WYOMING
0.498
(0.840)

GUNNISON RIVER
+0.770

COLORADO–BIG THOMPSON PROJECT -0.173

COLORADO
2.359
(3.105)

One acre-foot is equal to one foot of water covering an acre of land, or 325,850 gallons.

Great Salt Lake

Wasatch Range

Salt Lake City

Utah Lake

UTAH

Uinta Mts.

Vernal

Gannett Peak
4,207 m
13,804 ft

Wind River Range

Green River

Rock Springs

Great Divide Basin

North Platte

Most of Wyoming's entitlement is satisfied by the Green River, the Colorado's largest tributary.

FLAMING GORGE DAM

DINOSAUR NAT. MON.

Yampa

White

Utah diverts water from the up-per basin to the greater Salt Lake area for municipal, industrial, and agricultural uses.

COLORADO RIVER BASIN LIMIT

ZION NAT. PARK

GLEN CANYON DAM

GRAND CANYON NAT. PARK

Lees Ferry

Page

UPPER COLORADO BASIN

LOWER COLORADO BASIN

Recreation at Lake Powell, the longest man-made lake in the U. S., draws more than three million people yearly.

Green River

Moab

CANYONLANDS NATIONAL PARK

GLEN CANYON NAT. REC. AREA

Cataract Canyon

Grand Junction

Mt. Wilson
4,342 m
14,246 ft

Roan Cr.

GRAND DITCH

ROCKY MT. NAT. PARK

Front Range

Big Thompson R.

Denver

Boulder

Lake Granby

Aurora

Williams Fork

South Platte

ROCKY

COLORADO

MOUNTAINS

Fort Collins

Painted Desert

Navajo Indian Reservation

Plateau

Hopi Ind. Res.

Flagstaff

Little Colorado

Baldy Peak
3,476 m
11,404 ft

Tunnels, pipelines, and ditches divert Colorado River water eastward through the Rockies to 700,000 acres of farmland and to cities such as Denver.

Gallup

Rio Chama

New Mexico's share of the Colorado system comes from tributaries, including the San Juan River, which helps irri-gate 60,000 acres on the Navajo Indian Reservation.

COLORADO RIVER BASIN LIMIT

Santa Fe

Albuquerque

Arkansas

NEW MEXICO

CONTINENTAL DIVIDE

Gila

Rio Grande

The Colorado River basin drains a mostly semiarid region of 244,000 square miles — one-twelfth the size of the conterminous U. S.

N

More than 24 inches annual precipitation

Irrigated land

Dam

Canal or aqueduct

National Park System site

Power plant

Desalination plant

0   100 km
0   100 mi

NGS CARTOGRAPHIC DIVISION
RELIEF ART BY JOHN A. BONNER

Still rocking the boat, 74-year-old Martin Litton has spent nearly half his life campaigning to keep the Grand Canyon wild. Below Glen Canyon Dam, time-exposed beams from a flashlight (right) show fluctuations in daily water levels—the result of releasing water for hydroelectric operations, which Litton says "erodes beaches and hurts the ecology of the canyon."

transmountain diversions, but there are 20 others, draining a third of the Colorado's high tributary flows. Denver, where I live, gets half its water from the Colorado system.

THE MOST IMPROBABLE DIVERSION lies 2,000 feet below the Grand Ditch, where snowmelt collected in Lake Granby is literally pumped backward, up the old Colorado riverbed to Grand Lake. A beautiful, natural mountain lake is thus made part of a plumbing system that takes 90 percent of the fledgling main stem's water. A tunnel 13 miles long and nearly ten feet wide, part of the Colorado-Big Thompson Project, takes the lake water under the Continental Divide to the east face of the Rockies. The water then flows to cities like Boulder, serving a population of 500,000, and to Weld County, the fourth richest agricultural county in the U. S. But draining so much water leaves the Colorado a small stream in the mountains, with just enough water to meet the state requirement for keeping trout alive.

"Without that requirement you would have dry streambeds on the Western Slope for sure," said Rolly Fischer of the Colorado River Water Conservation District, which has carried on a half-century water war with Denver and the Front Range. Formed as a "protective association" when the Colorado-Big Thompson was built, the district has fought nearly every transmountain diversion. "The fear has been that the Western Slope would be dewatered just as California's Owens Valley was dried up by Los Angeles," said Fischer.

Denver's suburban neighbor Aurora has proposed tapping the Gunnison River, the one remaining Western Slope river not diverted to the Front Range. "The Gunnison is one of the last frontiers in the water wars," said Bill Trampe, one of the local ranchers who increased their own taxes for 1991 to fight Aurora in water court. "Recreation is the Gunnison's leading industry," he said. "It requires water in the streams. And half of Aurora's water would go on lawns."

But Aurora's population of 222,000 could triple by the year 2050, and the city is already using the water from 20,000 acres of mountain ranchland and has bought other farm water. "The Western Slope views it as their water, while in reality state law provides for diverting water to where it

the mentality and legal status quo. The primary law of the arid West, "first in time, first in right," gives the oldest users of water nearly ironclad seniority and ownership. Johnson, one of the grand men of the river, arrived in Colorado in a covered wagon and spent his life making the semiarid plains bloom. "It's very productive soil," he told me, "if you put good water on it."

Colorado's entire Front Range is a rich farm belt and a growing urban area because of water diverted across the Great Divide. The Grand Ditch is one of the oldest

can be used," explained Aurora's utilities director, Tom Griswold.

IN THE SPRING OF 1990, the signs of drought came early in the mountains, where snow depths are watched like a water stock market. On April 1, when I skied through the Fraser Experimental Forest west of Denver measuring snow with U. S. Forest Service scientists, the Colorado's predicted flow was 45 percent below normal.

Within days George Anderson was making tough decisions downstream about ranchland water in Roan Creek, just one small tributary near Grand Junction, Colorado. "I'd rather do anything than go tell a guy I've got to shut his water off," said Anderson, a soft-spoken, friendly water commissioner with a gold tooth in his grin. "If you don't have water up here, you don't have nothing," he said as he drove me around the irrigated valley.

In a drought, George Anderson is judge, jury, and executioner. On about a hundred ditches that in a good year carry Roan Creek to 8,000 acres of grass sprouted from sagebrush range, he had to close all but six of

the guillotine-shaped headgates in April.

As the Colorado's two main branches—the upper Colorado and the Green—converge, the landscape becomes increasingly arid and lonely; precipitation drops from as much as 55 inches in the mountains to as little as 10 on the Colorado Plateau, where the rivers sink into serpentine cracks.

The greatest pollution is salt. Starting with snowmelt quality of 50 parts per million, both rivers grow saline as the water is extracted, evaporates from reservoirs, passes over natural salt beds, and pours through soil that was

Battened down against blowing dust, campers jam Lone Rock Beach on Lake Powell, Glen Canyon Dam's 186-mile-long reservoir. Drought has dropped the lake level 66 feet, doubling beach size.

once the bottom of an ancient sea. By the time the Green reaches Green River, Utah, 600 miles from its source, its salinity exceeds the federal 500 parts per million salt standard for drinking water.

The river used to flood silty cold in the spring and trickle warm and clear in the fall.

Now, below dams like Flaming Gorge, it runs clear and cold year-round. The dams trap silt; reservoirs release frigid water from their depths back into the river, creating excellent trout habitat but contributing to the near extinction of several native species sensitive to the temperature change.

"We're not talking about one or two fish," said Harold Tyus, who runs the U. S. Fish and Wildlife Service laboratory on the Green River near Vernal, Utah. "We're talking about the loss of an entire fauna. More than half the endemic fish in the upper basin are endangered. This is the last stronghold."

Before sunrise in a rose-colored canyon I watched Tyus's biologists seine the Green for tiny Colorado squawfish larvae — "threads with eyeballs." That they exist at all there is due to the Yampa River, the only major undammed tributary in the Colorado drainage. It joins the Green in Dinosaur National Monument and runs warm and low enough for squawfish spawning. Proposals to dam the Yampa — one company wanted to sell the water to San Diego — would probably eliminate the fish, said Tyus, who favors giving the fish a water right of their own.

WHERE THE GREEN and Colorado meet, in the remote labyrinth of Canyonlands National Park near Moab, Utah, a powerful river results. I could see the pistachio color of one mixing with the red-silt-laden flow of the other, a total of 13,000 cubic feet a second swirling and gathering strength for a plunge through Cataract Canyon. In a life jacket and rubber raft I joined a group of thrill seekers through Big Drops 1, 2, and 3 — rolling, muddy rapids guaranteed to soak to the skin.

In side canyons we examined the ruins of Anasazi Indians, the "ancient ones" who lived along the river a thousand years ago. The best explanation for their disappearance is a combination of drought, overpopulation, and internal strife — elements present in the West today.

"The Colorado has defined what the West became," the rafters heard from Sally Ranney, president of American Wildlands, after a steak dinner on the beach. "And because of the water shortage it will define what the West will *not* become. We have a saying out here that water flows toward money. It has nothing to do with gravity."

Par for this course, 125 million gallons of wastewater are pumped yearly from the city of Page, Arizona, to keep desert doglegs green near Glen Canyon Dam, in background. Recycling the West's water allows greater use of its scarcest resource.

Near the end of our trip the river widened into Lake Powell. Capable of holding nearly two years' flow in a red sandstone bathtub 1,900 miles around, Powell is just upstream from Lees Ferry, the dividing point between the upper and lower basins. The 1922 compact apportioned 7.5 million acre-feet to each basin, from an annual flow then thought to average about 17 million. In years of drought, the lower basin gets its share first, sometimes resulting in a shortfall for the upper basin.

Virtually all the water that will enter the Colorado has done so by now, and the lake is a quick look at demand and supply. In 1990, the fourth year of drought, a ring was showing in the bathtub 66 feet above the water level (evaporation alone takes five feet a year). Less than 5.5 million acre-feet of water flowed into Lake Powell, not nearly the 8.25 million required downstream by the compact and a later treaty.

Lake Powell's creation in 1963 was the crowning act of the U. S. Bureau of Reclamation's 30-year, big-dam era. Built for water storage, flood control, and power, Glen Canyon Dam flooded caverns and canyons that only a few thousand people had ever seen. Today more than three million people visit the vast desert lake each year, and I could see a new conflict on the river, as the traditional water users — the irrigators and power interests — bumped heads with the enormous economic force of leisure time. Boaters wanted their docks in the water, not draped on silt.

Downriver, in the Grand Canyon, the dam was exacting another price. With most of the silt blocked off, the clear, deep-green "hungry" water ate away existing sand and silt, the base for the canyon's ecosystem. "Some of the worst erosion came early, in 1964," said Martin Litton as he maneuvered a dory through the rapids below the dam for perhaps the 75th time in his 74 years. The Grand Canyon curmudgeon has long been a bur under the saddle of dam interests.

Without the usual feast-and-famine flows of the natural river, wildlife changed

Desert harvest: Matthew Endischee displays the Navajo Reservation's first commercial crop of shiitake mushrooms, grown on oak logs. Water from the San Juan River drips from above through a mesh canopy that reduces evaporation by blocking 80 percent of the sunlight.

But Lloyd Greiner, a manager with the Western Area Power Administration, later countered: "I don't believe there is enough evidence that fluctuating flows are a major contributor to the damage. The river drops 2,000 feet in the canyon. With water rushing through, there will be erosion."

On a Sunday morning we awoke in the canyon to bad news: Low weekend demand for electricity in Phoenix meant that low "Saturday water" was reaching us 87 miles from the dam. In Unkar Rapids, Litton hit a rock. A few miles farther the river looked worse. "I've never seen Hance Rapids this low. This is basically unrunnable in dories," he said when he saw the boulders sticking out of the water.

So we waited, with environmentalist Litton praying, ironically, that Phoenix would suffer a heat wave so we could float the river. That night I stared up into a heaven cut by the cleavage of the canyon. I watched satellites inch across the star-sprinkled sky and thought that mine was the last generation to have seen a night sky uncluttered by man-made things—or the Grand Canyon's waters unregulated. Two days later Litton's prayers were answered.

abruptly. Fish used to warmer waters and muddy bottoms died off. Beaver disappeared because entrances to their homes, built underwater in the riverbanks, were regularly exposed as the water level rose and fell. Tamarisk invaded and songbirds increased; trout were introduced and bald eagles began to make winter stopovers.

Litton glanced up at the violet-green swallows looping about for bugs: "They're doing fine, but most cliff swallows left after the water cleared. Not enough mud for their nests. With fewer beaches for boaters to camp on, the national park limited visitors to 22,000 a year, outlawed driftwood fires except in winter, and made everyone carry out all waste."

On our second morning we awoke to find our boats high and dry on the narrow beach. The water had receded nearly 13 feet during the night. Glen Canyon's hydroturbines are used when power demand peaks, causing the water in the Grand Canyon to go up and down like a tide. Less demand for power, less water. "See, the water is low today because it was cool in Phoenix yesterday and they didn't want as much air-conditioning. The beaches can't take this daily up-and-down stuff," explained Litton, who argued for a shift of peaking power away from Glen Canyon.

WHEN Maj. John Wesley Powell emerged from the Grand Canyon in 1869, he met Mormon colonists who gave him melons and other food from ground that received only four inches of rain a year. Powell later foretold the opportunities and limits of western water: "All the waters of all the arid lands will eventually be taken from their natural channels," he wrote. The Mormons believed that irrigation fulfilled the prophecy of Isaiah, that when Christ returned "the desert shall rejoice, and blossom as the rose. . . . for in the wilderness shall waters break out, and streams in the desert."

Like a miracle the river plugged by Hoover Dam, on the border of Nevada and Arizona, achieved that promise. The "grande dam" reined in the Colorado, fostered what was the richest irrigation project in the world, and watered and powered the Sunbelt. As I

24

followed the waterway 150 miles below Hoover, I could almost hear the slurping straws of distant cities. On one side of Lake Havasu is the Central Arizona Project (CAP), which carries river water 335 miles eastward to Phoenix and, soon, to Tucson. On the other is the Colorado River Aqueduct, emerging from a pump house able to suck up one billion gallons of water a day for southern California.

Until 1990 those California intake pipes, run by the Metropolitan Water District (MWD) of Southern California, took pretty much what they needed — over one million acre-feet a year, twice MWD's right to the river. Arizona wasn't using its full share. With the CAP nearing completion in 1990 it looked like Arizona would come close. When dry California asked for more water, the Bureau of Reclamation, with its hand on the Hoover spigot, said no. It was a

Net loss: U. S. Fish and Wildlife specialist Bruce Haines seines the Green River for scarce Colorado squawfish larvae but this time finds only non-native minnows. Dams, which alter the water level and temperature of rivers, endanger squawfish and other indigenous species.

historic announcement. As 1990 began, the lower basin had, for the first time, used up its full share of the Colorado River. Six months later, with generous rains in Arizona, the spigot to California was reopened.

Given these limits, it was strange to me to travel west along the Colorado River Aqueduct and find its waters spread in chevron-shaped shallow ponds near Palm Springs, California, soaking into the ground! Like a desert mirage, the waste wasn't what it appeared: The water was recharging the desert's huge underground aquifer.

Because of the rich aquifer, wealth beyond all imagining has come to Palm Springs. On Country Club Drive, I passed developments with names like "The Lakes" and "Desert Falls." At Marriott's 400-acre Desert Springs resort the lobby contains a ten-foot-deep indoor lagoon, complete with boats, and the resort pumps one and a half million gallons of water a day onto its golf course in summer.

I N LOS ANGELES I found serious attempts to conserve water as the California drought entered its fourth year. Squads from the city's Drought Busters enforced new ordinances against washing sidewalks, serving unsolicited water in restaurants, and watering lawns during the day.

I spent one morning cruising the streets with Drought Buster Tony Marufo, who would brake to a halt at the first sign of a damp spot on a hot sidewalk. "Some people say I can *smell* water," he said, grinning. In 1990, in a city long known for its profligate water use, Marufo and his 25 colleagues wrote 8,862 citations from May to October. By late summer Los Angeles had reduced its water use by more than 10 percent.

But MWD's Tim Quinn told me that conservation is a limited tool, that per capita use is up in most western cities. Newer houses actually push water use up — all have automatic dishwashers — and higher income families use more water. "We're trying to find ways to flatten those numbers out," he said, "but lowering them may be impossible. It would cross the line of fundamental changes in life-style — no green yards, for example."

And that, I learned, was a line that no one in the California water establishment wanted to cross. Controlling growth, they said, is not a water agency's job; finding more water is. The population of 15 million served by MWD is growing by 300,000 a year, and officials fear running short of water by the year 2000 if serious drought conditions continue.

The Sacramento River is a likely source of relief but an unpopular choice with many

A trickle is no trifle for Drought Buster
George Verdesoto (below), one of two
dozen water patrols who scout Los Angeles streets and issue citations to anyone
wasting water. In desert communities
like Lake La Quinta (right), near Palm
Springs, developers create oases like this
many-tongued mini-lake to attract
western homebuyers.

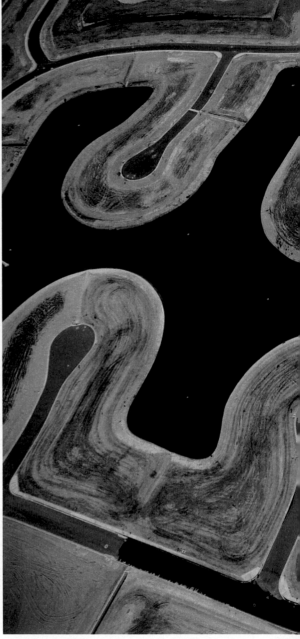

northern Californians who think southern
Californians are stealing their water. The
drought has also raised anew such possibili-
ties as seagoing tankers bringing fresh water
from the Pacific Northwest, ships hauling ice-
bergs, and a pipeline to tap the Columbia
River. Desalination plants have been started
to turn Pacific Ocean water into fresh water.

Another prospect is water marketing—
trading water like a commodity, a relatively
new concept in California. In its first
deal MWD agreed to finance the lining of
irrigation canals and the upgrading of

Imperial Irrigation District plumbing at a
cost of 223 million dollars. The deal will save
100,000 acre-feet from seeping into the
ground, thus increasing water available to
MWD. The agency might also pay farmers
not to grow crops in dry years: Agriculture
draws 80 to 90 percent of the Colorado.

"The phone rings three times a week from
landowners in other states, wanting to sell
their water," said Tim Quinn. Wyoming
might use its water after all, I thought—by
selling it to California. But state laws
would have to change for that.

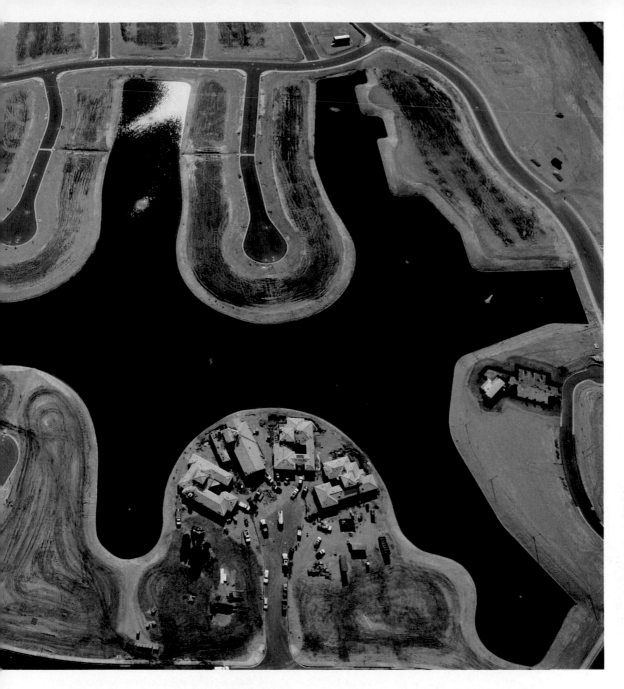

Everywhere I went along the river, a new breeze was blowing on water policy. At the end of the pipeline, where I expected a hurricane force, it was but a whisper. One of the fastest growing communities in southern California is Chula Vista, outside San Diego—highly dependent on the Colorado River. EastLake, a development being built there on barren land a few miles from the Mexican border, is an example of how water leverages growth. EastLake's water cost of $525 an acre-foot (a western family of four uses one acre-foot of water a year) helps turn worthless

ground into a thriving community. Projections for the year 2004 show 25,000 people living on 3,200 acres in 8,900 homes, a five-fold population increase.

"This is going to be our downtown here," said developer Robert Snyder, pointing to a gully of sand. In an area called EastLake Hills and Shores, with 1,834 houses ranging in price from $70,000 to $600,000, peer pressure keeps most homes surrounded by verdant bluegrass, and Snyder says he could not force xeriscaping, the use of water-miser desert plants, on EastLake

Big-buckled success has come to Imperial Valley farmer Jim Storm (below) from Colorado River water that irrigates five dozen crops marketed under his River Ranch brand name. Across the border in Mexico, water means survival to workers who pick cotton for six dollars a day.

our people work on our farm," said Leona Kakar, a strong woman whose family led the way to this Indian-country success. She spoke to me in the shade of a tamarisk tree after ceremonial basket dances to celebrate groundbreaking for a tribal museum. A mile away workers were harvesting cotton. "I've given 26 years of my life for this fight," she said with a shake of her graying, curly hair. "It's made a world of difference."

Until the 1960s a few hundred Ak-Chin subsisted in the Sonoran Desert around shallow wells. But pumping around Phoenix lowered the water table hundreds of feet, making farming too expensive. Citing the 1908 Supreme Court Winters doctrine, which reserves enough water for Indians to irrigate their land, the tribe sued the federal government. Congress awarded the Ak-Chin CAP water, which first arrived in 1987. Within two years a 38 percent unemployment rate had dropped to 4 percent, and the tribal farm had tripled its acreage.

Encouraged by the Ak-Chin success, other Arizona tribes, which have been without adequate water for a century, are following suit. Their claims total more than all the water in Arizona, which arguably could make them the American Arabs of water. The huge Navajo Indian Reservation alone could claim most of the flow of the Colorado, based on the Winters doctrine. "It's certainly a cloud of uncertainty that hangs over our water management programs," said Larry Linser, deputy director of Arizona's Department of Water Resources.

But a water right without wet water is useless, and several tribes have compromised in order to get canals built and water delivered. The CAP carries Colorado water for ten tribes. "We are doing what we did in A.D. 200, just a little more modern," said Leona Kakar. "Water is our lifeline, our blood."

Below the Colorado River Aqueduct, the Colorado runs like a sluice, wide and sluggish, the banks riprapped in places and lined with tamarisk and occasional rows of cottages. Near Yuma, Arizona, it backs up behind the Imperial Dam, which takes more than 20 percent of the water, the single

homeowners: "In five years maybe I can."

Snyder, an athletic third-generation California builder, drove me by the EastLake Shores Beach Club, where palms and grass surround a sandy beach. "This is the kind of amenity that brings people to EastLake. We've spoiled ourselves, no doubt about it. There has been enough water in California for whatever we wanted to do."

S AGUARO CACTUSES stand guard in Arizona along the Central Arizona Project. The 3.5-billion-dollar water network administered by the Bureau of Reclamation is considered by environmentalists the ultimate in desert folly. In order to pump 1.5 million acre-feet of water clear to Tucson and subsidize its cost so farmers can irrigate economically, the bureau helped build a coal power plant near Page, which taints the air over the Grand Canyon and the Navajo Reservation.

But south of Phoenix, on the tiny Ak-Chin Indian Reservation, that same CAP is a godsend, I learned. Water from the Colorado has turned a dirt-poor community into a prideful, self-sufficient farming community with low unemployment and no welfare.

"We're using it to farm cotton, small grains, alfalfa—even fish—and 95 percent of

Radiant shafts of water stream down rows of rich farmland in southern California's Imperial Valley. Receiving only three inches of rain a year, the valley's half million cultivated acres would revert to desert without the 2.9 million

acre-feet of water—about one-fifth of the Colorado's entire flow—drawn from the All American Canal. Altogether, 700 prosperous farmers generate about a billion dollars a year in produce, grain, and livestock.

The Colorado: A River Drained Dry

biggest chunk of the river, and pushes it through the All American Canal about 80 miles west to California's Imperial Valley.

Driving west, I watched dune buggies race over sand dunes sliced by the canal, where an estimated 70,000 acre-feet of water soaks into the sand each year. Congress has authorized the Bureau of Reclamation to stop the leakage on the canal; lining it is a likely solution.

California cities can't understand how so much water can just disappear into the ground—or how nearly one million acre-feet of water runs off and under irrigated fields in the Imperial Irrigation District and into the briny Salton Sea. The state of California has found that the district, at the far end of the canal, wastes about 15 percent of its water and has required it to conserve 100,000 acre-feet. Some 700 farmers there, who generate nearly one billion dollars each year, have a very senior right to the river's water. After 90 years, they are worried.

"We do live in a democracy," said Larry Cox, a 32-year-old cotton, alfalfa, and vegetable producer I found weighing onion seed. "If you've got 16 million voters up there in L.A., who's to say they can't change the laws? I think it's a definite possibility."

The land is so salty and the river water is so saline (averaging more than 700 parts per million) at the end of its journey that extra water is poured through the soil to flush salt away from roots. Each field gets about four feet of water. Pipes buried four to eight feet below the surface then carry the excess, salty water away.

Cox, whose onions will be used on McDonald's hamburgers, said he resisted more efficient irrigation methods until he felt forced to try the drip system on a tomato field plagued by waterborne soil disease. "It was fairly easy," he said, "and the yield went up substantially."

NOWHERE ON THE COLORADO did I get a greater sense of the dividing of the waters between the haves and have-nots than below Morelos Dam in Mexico, south of Yuma, Arizona. The last of the Colorado River is pushed into the Canal Central here, and the riverbed becomes shallow enough to wade across. Many Mexicans hoping to start a new life with the water and wealth of the U. S. have waited in the riverbed until dark before crossing the border.

Without a real river, the poor have built makeshift homes along the canal. They are called *avecindados*—squatters. I watched an old man wash his clothes and hang them on a *cachanilla*, or arrowwood, plant. A woman carried a bucket of water for her garden, a skimpy row of corn and squash. Their homes were part adobe made from canal mud, cardboard, and car parts.

For some 20 miles the nearly empty riverbed is the border between the U. S. and Mexico, but metaphorically the Colorado has divided the two countries since the first

What remains of the Colorado seeps into desert sands after Mexico's Canal Central, glistening in the background (above), takes its treaty share.

Workers in Yuma, Arizona, install one of 9,360 desalting membranes in a desalination plant that, when completed, will reclaim more than 70 million gallons of drainage water a day from the Wellton-Mohawk irrigation district.

attempts to divert the river into California. A 1944 treaty guarantees Mexico 1.5 million acre-feet of water a year. After return flows from the irrigation district east of Yuma raised salinity in Mexico to more than a thousand parts per million, killing crops, an agreement was signed controlling salt levels. Rather than take the saline U. S. soil out of production, Congress authorized a 260-million-dollar desalination plant.

Under the treaty, Mexican officials don't expect more water from the U. S. "The States aren't interested in giving up anything," said Luis López Moctezuma, a planning official for Baja California. Only two-thirds of irrigable land in Baja gets water from the river, which is divided among 14,000 farmers, each of whom can plant only 40 of their 50 acres. There also is an increasing demand for urban water: An aqueduct takes Colorado River water to Tijuana.

IT WAS IN THE RIVER DELTA that I saw the real effect of the water shortage. The delta was once a series of green lagoons that ecologist Aldo Leopold described as a "milk-and-honey wilderness" where egrets gathered like a "premature snowstorm," jaguars roamed, and wild melons grew. That was in 1922, the year the Colorado River's interstate compact was signed and plans were laid for Hoover Dam. In the years since, marine ecologist Cuauhtemoc León Díaz told me, the ecosystem has changed completely.

Two marine animals became endangered species: a fish called the totoaba and a porpoise called the vaquita. The totoaba used to grow as long as six feet and weigh 300 pounds; its flesh and bladder were a delicacy. Adults migrated to the mouth of the delta in thick schools, and the tides sent their eggs back, deep into the natural nursery of the delta. When the river was cut off, the nursery mechanism was cut off too.

Other, unknown species may have disappeared, according to saltwater agronomist Nicholas Yensen, who rediscovered a wheat-like salt grass thought extinct. Through selective breeding he improved the yield from one or two pounds an acre to one or two tons an acre. The grass grows best when irrigated with full-strength seawater, making it valuable in arid and saline areas worldwide.

"When the Colorado stopped flowing, we lost the main population of the plant—it

Lifeblood to those who depend on it, the Colorado flows down Mexican canals, nearly 1,450 miles from its source. With demand for water exceeding the river's ability to deliver, people in the West will have to cut back or do without.

could have gone extinct, and we'd never have known," he said. The river was like the Nile in its importance to the delta. "We probably never will know what we lost."

In my last days on the river I talked with Cucapá Indians at their village, aided by Anita Alvarez de Williams, a self-taught expert on the small tribe. It had been six months since they had been able to catch enough fish to sell. Still, at every home, a boat lay expectantly in the gravel. "I don't have much hope for the future," said Rosendo Carrillo Oliveras. "The older ones fish, the younger ones goof off—there is no work."

Anita introduced me to Inocencia Gonzales Saiz, a 53-year-old woman who makes traditional beaded collars, worn in ceremonies. Instead of fish, she said, they eat frijoles and junk food. The water can't be used effectively on melons or squash because it is too salty. They eat a diet high in sugar and fat. Many of the people have diabetes.

I thought back to all that I had seen on the Colorado. The river could produce so much—and promise so little. As we left El Mayor, Anita said to me, "There are important things to learn from apparently simple cultures. These guys have been around for a couple thousand years. But barring a miracle, you're seeing the last of them."

Aldo Leopold, at the end of his essay on the Colorado Delta, wrote: "Man always kills the thing he loves. . . . I am glad I shall never be young without wild country to be young in."

With what water it had, the Colorado created a new civilization in the Southwest. Now it is beset by the needs of a mature and burgeoning community. There is talk of renegotiating the compact to move more water where the people are and of creating new ways to exchange, augment, conserve, and manage. The river above the delta reminded me of an aging prima donna eking out a little more time, refusing to face the inevitable.

"What river?" I remembered the fisherman El Coyote asking me.

I knew the answer, but had no reply. ☐

Spewing stacks in Copşa Mică, Romania, coat buildings and boys alike with carbon, a reminder of industrial poisons that have poured

EAST EUROPE'S
The Iron Curtain Rises to Reveal a Land

By JON THOMPSON   Photographs by JAMES NACHTWEY MAGNUM

into the region's air, water, and soil for decades.

DARK DAWN
Tarnished by Pollution

FINGERS OF SUNLIGHT pry into the fume-choked air as a pot operator works to release bubbles of gas from molten metal at an aluminum plant in Žiar nad Hronom, Czechoslovakia. He uses a wooden stick, which burns shorter with each use but leaves no contaminants in the mix. Every day, workers here inhale cancer-causing

tar vapors. Reports of job-related cancer vary widely—but as a concession to the hazardous surroundings, employees get to retire at 55, five years earlier than normal. Not only humans are at risk: The plant also emits fluorine gas and salts, dangerous to trees and livestock.

A STEAMING POTION of water, limestone, and coke residue pours into a quarter-mile-wide holding pond at the Buna chemical works near Merseburg, Germany. This waste, which seeps into farmland, reportedly is harmless. That cannot be said of the ten pounds of mercury the plant dumps, on average, into the Saale

in a single day. Metal-laced industrial waste also taints Eastern Europe's food chain. In areas of Poland's Upper Silesia, soil levels of lead, cadmium, and other dangerous metals have been found to exceed accepted limits, and 35 percent of the children in a recent study showed evidence of lead poisoning.

While the world wasn't looking, Eastern Europe's regimes poisoned their environment in the name of progress. Now new leaders must assess the damage and set priorities for reversing it.

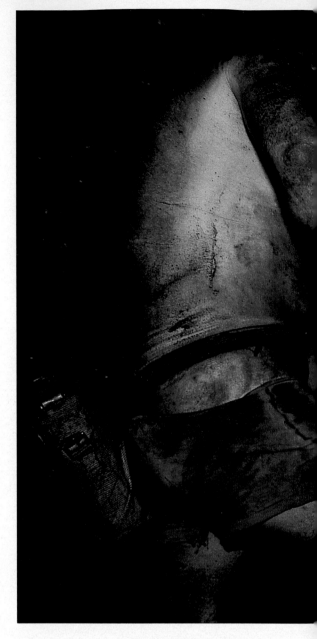

I N THE FALL OF 1989 the communist governments in Eastern Europe began to crumble. As the Iron Curtain was torn apart, journalists—nosing around in Poland, East Germany, Czechoslovakia, Hungary, Romania, and Bulgaria with a newfound freedom—were met by an outpouring of complaints about polluted air, contaminated water, and poisoned soil.

The headlines in the Western press—"Pollution Chokes East-Bloc Nations," "Environmental Catastrophe in Eastern Europe"—brought a crowd of questions to my mind: Why all the fuss right now? How bad is it? How did it happen? Is it affecting people's health, and how are the new governments responding?

As a doctor by training and a scientist by inclination, I was disturbed by what I read. For two months in 1990 I traveled throughout Eastern Europe, eager to discover the truth. What I found was not nearly so simple as the headlines had led me to believe. Eastern Europe's industry is backward and outdated, its workers are exposed to hazards no longer accepted in the West, and little thought is given to pollution control. The natural environment is being destroyed, as in the West before antipollution and industrial health regulations were introduced. But the clamor announcing an environmental catastrophe seemed out of proportion. It turns out that in the late 1980s complaints about the environment became focused into a way of showing disapproval of communist rule. So pollution, certainly a major problem, attracted intense and sometimes exaggerated public interest.

My journey began in Kraków, the historic

JON THOMPSON, a physician formerly specializing in internal medicine, is now a writer living in London. He wrote "Inside the Kremlin" for the January 1990 NATIONAL GEOGRAPHIC.

capital of Poland, a city spared the ravages of war and adorned with many old churches and fine buildings. I took a walk along the grassy bank of the Wisła (Vistula) River. The air was clean and fresh, and the river, dark and greeny brown. A lone fisherman sat by the water gazing at the reflected beauty of the town.

"How's the fishing?" I asked.

"We catch some carp, but it's been terrible until recently," he said. "It's all to do with the poisons put out by the factory upstream."

I was surprised at how much he knew.

A local taxi driver showed an equally remarkable interest in pollution by giving me a rundown on how much sulfur dioxide was put

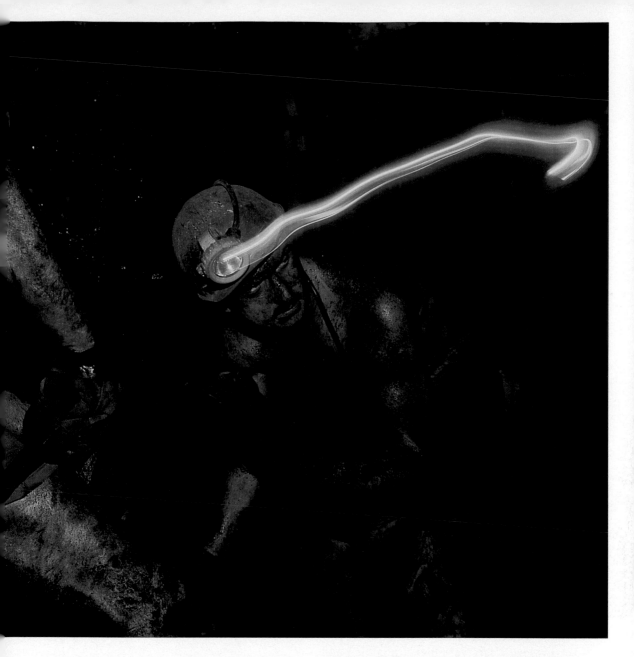

out by the city's power stations and the nearby giant steel mill at Nowa Huta (New Foundry), built in the early 1950s with a Soviet version of 1930s Pittsburgh technology.

"Every day on TV there are discussions about the sulfur dioxide level in the air, the state of the rivers, and other pollution problems," he explained. "Kraków lies in a valley, and in the winter a blanket of foul air often covers the whole city. When it rains, the smoke is dissolved and falls as acid. Our old stone buildings are just being eaten away.

"Everything was secret under the communists, and we spent all our energy simply staying alive. Now we have some information, and

ENERGY LIFELINE and environmental nightmare both begin in the coal mines. These Polish miners dig high-grade black coal, some of which Poland will export to raise cash. The nation keeps all of its dirtier, high-sulfur brown coal for industry and home heating.

we realize how important these things are."

Jan Lach, head of a team making independent measurements of dust and gas emissions from 19 factories around Kraków, soon confirmed what the taxi driver and fisherman had told me. He was nervous and unused to foreign journalists and anxious to give facts rather than opinions.

"On a yearly basis the maximum permitted

levels for sulfur dioxide are exceeded the whole time," he said, "and only once did the fluorine level fall to within the permitted range. We have a long way to go to meet our targets." I was intrigued to note that in 1989 the amount of dust falling on the city was less than in previous years. "During that year we had a lot of strikes, and many factories were not working properly," he explained. "It had nothing to do with improvements in pollution control."

Pollution in Kraków was nowhere to be seen, but appearances can be deceptive—it was summer after all. From the walls of an old fort on the outskirts of the city, I could see Nowa Huta's forest of smoking chimneys looming in the distance. In winter with wind blowing smoke toward the city, I could imagine quite a different picture—the dirty one my taxi driver had painted earlier.

The next day, I met Stanisław Juchnowicz, a distinguished-looking architect with spectacles and silver hair, president of the Polish Ecology Club. "Why," I asked him, "was a huge steelworks built next to a city of such historic importance?"

He paused, weighing his answer. "You must understand, it was a political decision. There is no iron ore here, and we had very little industry. According to the theory of our communist masters, the wage-earning class was supposed to have a leading role in society. In the 1950s all the countries under communist rule underwent massive industrialization. Kraków was a university town with very few wage earners. Putting the steelworks here was a deliberate attempt to destroy the old order by creating a class of wage earners where none existed before."

Like Juchnowicz, other members of the Polish Ecology Club were highly qualified and intelligent. They all showed deep concern, speaking with passion about the horrors of pollution. They told me about the uncontrolled discharge of fluorine gas from an aluminum plant, the escape of organic solvents from a pharmaceutical factory, the fallout of cadmium-laden dust onto the soil from smelting works, and the uptake of cadmium by some vegetables eaten by humans. They also reported that 170 tons of lead were released into the air from Nowa Huta annually, and that electrostatic precipitators fitted to factory chimneys to control the escape of dust were switched off at night to save electricity. Then there was the appalling state of Poland's

44

Pollution's long shadow

FROM THE BALTIC to the Black Sea, half a century of runaway industrialization has left a smear of destruction through the heart of Eastern Europe. Under orders from Moscow, factories appeared where only farms and markets had stood. The historic university city of Kraków was "given" the huge Nowa Huta steelworks simply because the Stalinist regime mistrusted the city's intellectual elite. Now the city lies within the "dirty triangle" formed by Poland, Czechoslovakia, and eastern Germany—a region of dense population where pollution controls are often nonexistent. Eastern Europe's network of rivers has become a convenient method of disposal—especially the Danube, recipient of eight nations' waste.

Dead and dying conifer forests, downwind from two blue-plumed Czechoslovak power plants, appear orange at center in this false-color satellite image. Healthier stands appear black. Pollution affects some 173,000 acres in this region. Lines between the plumes are strip-mine scars.

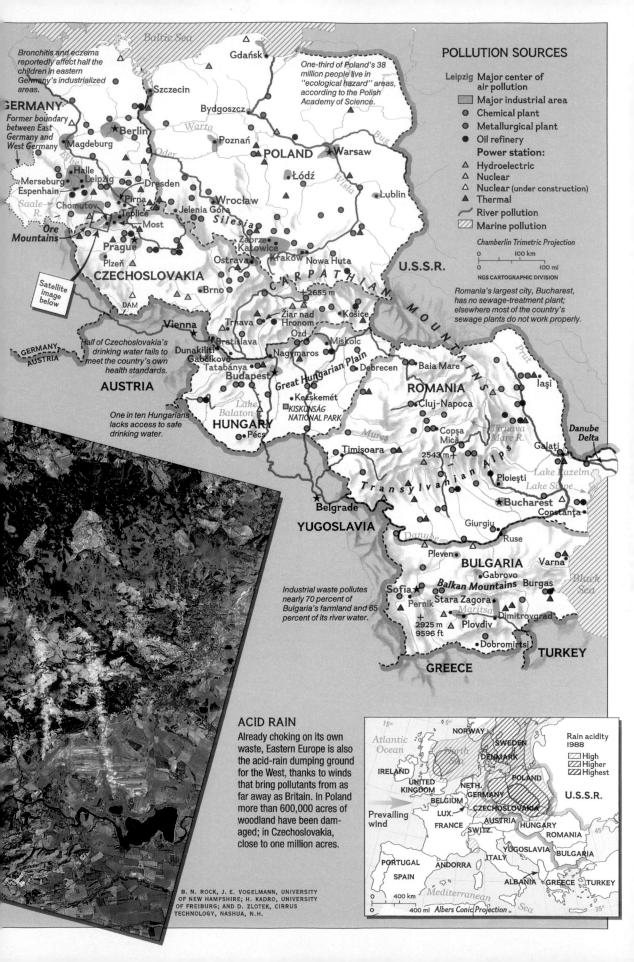

Bronchitis and eczema reportedly affect half the children in eastern Germany's industrialized areas.

One-third of Poland's 38 million people live in "ecological hazard" areas, according to the Polish Academy of Science.

POLLUTION SOURCES

Leipzig — Major center of air pollution

▨ Major industrial area
◉ Chemical plant
⬤ Metallurgical plant
● Oil refinery

Power station:
△ Hydroelectric
△ Nuclear
△ Nuclear (under construction)
▲ Thermal
〰 River pollution
▨ Marine pollution

Chamberlin Trimetric Projection

0   100 km
0   100 mi

NGS CARTOGRAPHIC DIVISION

Romania's largest city, Bucharest, has no sewage-treatment plant; elsewhere most of the country's sewage plants do not work properly.

GERMANY

Former boundary between East Germany and West Germany

Merseburg
Espenhain

Saale R.

Ore Mountains

Satellite image below

Baltic Sea

Gdańsk
Szczecin
Bydgoszcz
Poznań
POLAND ★Warsaw
Łódź
Lublin
Berlin
Magdeburg
Halle
Leipzig
Dresden
Pirna
Chomutov
Teplice
Most
Jelenia Góra
Wrocław
Silesia
Prague
Plzeň
CZECHOSLOVAKIA
Brno
DAM
Zabrze
Katowice
Ostrava
Kraków
Nowa Huta
+2655 m
Košice
Žiar nad Hronom
Ozd
Trnava
Vienna
Bratislava
Dunakiliti
Gabčíkovo
Tatabánya
Budapest
Nagymaros
Miskolc
U.S.S.R.
CARPATHIAN MOUNTAINS
Oder
Warta
Bug
Wisła
Elbe

GERMANY
AUSTRIA

Half of Czechoslovakia's drinking water fails to meet the country's own health standards.

AUSTRIA

One in ten Hungarians lacks access to safe drinking water.

Lake Balaton
HUNGARY
Pécs
Kecskemét
KISKUNSÁG NATIONAL PARK
Great Hungarian Plain
Mures

Baia Mare
Debrecen
Cluj-Napoca
ROMANIA
Copşa Mică
Timişoara
2543 m
Transylvanian Alps
Tirnava Mare R.
Iaşi
Galaţi
Danube Delta
Ploieşti
Lake Razelm
Lake Sinoe
★Bucharest
Constanţa
Prut

★Belgrade
YUGOSLAVIA

Danube
Giurgiu
Ruse
Pleven
BULGARIA
Gabrovo
Sofia★
Pernik
Stara Zagora
Balkan Mountains
Burgas
Varna
+2925 m 9596 ft
Plovdiv
Maritsa
Dimitrovgrad
Dobromirtsi
TURKEY
GREECE
Black Sea

Industrial waste pollutes nearly 70 percent of Bulgaria's farmland and 65 percent of its river water.

ACID RAIN

Already choking on its own waste, Eastern Europe is also the acid-rain dumping ground for the West, thanks to winds that bring pollutants from as far away as Britain. In Poland more than 600,000 acres of woodland have been damaged; in Czechoslovakia, close to one million acres.

B. N. ROCK, J. E. VOGELMANN, UNIVERSITY OF NEW HAMPSHIRE; H. KADRO, UNIVERSITY OF FREIBURG; AND D. ZLOTEK, CIRRUS TECHNOLOGY, NASHUA, N.H.

Atlantic Ocean
NORWAY
SWEDEN
DENMARK
IRELAND
UNITED KINGDOM
NETH.
GERMANY
POLAND
U.S.S.R.
BELGIUM
LUX.
CZECHOSLOVAKIA
Prevailing wind
FRANCE
AUSTRIA
HUNGARY
SWITZ.
ROMANIA
PORTUGAL
ANDORRA
ITALY
YUGOSLAVIA
BULGARIA
SPAIN
ALBANIA
GREECE
TURKEY
North Sea
Mediterranean Sea

Rain acidity 1988
▨ High
▨ Higher
▨ Highest

0   400 km
0   400 mi   Albers Conic Projection

MIST CARRIES a deadly payload to the remains of a Czechoslovak forest. Sulfur from coal-burning industries combines with moisture to create airborne acids that kill and denude woodlands. The acid rain that created this timber graveyard in the Ore Mountains could have risen from any neighboring country. Further damage is done to surviving woodlands by insects like the larch bud moth. Thriving under conditions other forest animals cannot withstand, the moth has devastated a large area in Poland.

rivers, polluted by untreated sewage, industrial effluent, and brine pumped out of coal mines. The picture that club members presented was one of unrelieved mismanagement and disaster.

Polish intellectuals were clearly the driving force behind the surprising awareness of pollution I had noticed earlier. In Nowa Huta, where a gray-black dust cakes everything, I found another point of view. There I met a 50-year-old smelter, round, grimy, toothless, and proud. "They're always on TV and radio going on about this place," he told me, pointing his callused finger in the direction of Kraków. "Why don't they campaign for a modern plant here instead of trying to close us down?"

KATOWICE, an old industrial center where miners have been digging zinc, lead, and silver for more than 300 years, sits on rich deposits of coal. This coal belt extends in a broad band through southern Poland into eastern Germany and northern Czechoslovakia, where Eastern Europe's chemical, metallurgical, and other heavy industry is concentrated. Katowice and the surrounding area consist of a huge urban-industrial development with a dozen or so satellite centers crisscrossed with roads and lurching tramlines bent out of shape by subsidence of the mines. Fetid lakes, massive spoil heaps, rows of grubby houses, shops, schools, factories, hospitals, and mines are all jumbled together in haphazard confusion.

The air has a distinctive sulfurous smell. To provide the power and heat for industry and homes, great quantities of poor-quality coal— mainly brown coal, or lignite—are burned, while the more expensive low-sulfur coals are exported for precious foreign currency. Gray skies and dirty cobbled streets add gloom to an already dismal city. People live amid poverty and squalor, cramped in blackened tenement buildings. I felt as if the clock had stopped 40 years ago: I was back in the industrial Midlands of my English childhood.

A retired joiner invited me to his home in one of the tenement buildings. The rooms were spotless. His wife said she had to wash the curtains every two weeks and found it almost a full-time job cleaning the apartment. From their living room window I could see the nearby smelting works and right into the furnaces, which glowed orange and shimmered in the intense heat. I asked what it was like living amid all the foul air and dust.

The joiner lit a cigarette: "This is my life," he said, "I've worked here for 45 years. It was

hard, but we had enough to raise our family, and we have somewhere to live. If they close the works, there will be no jobs. What will people do then?" His view—a dirty job is better than no job at all—I heard echoed time and again by working people in all the countries.

My focus at this point was on air and soil pollution caused by the burning of coal. The enormity of the problem was exposed in a map of Europe I was given in Wrocław, showing the amount of sulfur falling on the ground in dust and in precipitation. The highest fallout, marked as a great gray blotch, covered the

"dirty triangle" formed by the coal belt of northern Czechoslovakia, eastern Germany, and the Silesian district of southern Poland.

Highly acidic rain falls in the same area and extends in a streak to the east, where the prevailing wind carries the acid-forming smoke. Here the forests are dying. Some people believe the trees are being killed by fluorides washed out of the smoke; others blame acidification of the soil and the reduced availability of trace elements, already depleted by the practice of growing only one type of tree on the same land all the time. Whatever the exact

A RENAISSANCE SCULPTURE on Kraków's Cloth Hall melts away, its porous limestone vulnerable to air-borne sulfuric acid from the smokestacks of the Nowa Huta steel mill, just miles away. Western companies are lining up to sell scrubbers and other antipollution devices to the region's governments, which are at last trying to halt industry's destructive march against art and nature. But leaders are walking a tightrope between spending money to clean up the environment and keeping their foundering economies afloat.

how beautiful the forest used to be. He couldn't believe how it has been destroyed."

We turned off the road onto a rough track. "Climb up there," he said. "Then you'll understand what acid rain is all about." On the way up I nearly fell into a deep gully gouged out of the mountainside by water rushing down the treeless slopes. From a high ridge I saw a forest of stark, gray, dead tree trunks extending as far as the eye could see. The feeling of desolation was overpowering. If the chimney smoke has had this effect on trees, what could it be doing to human health, I wondered?

EVERYWHERE I WENT, I tried to find out, but garbled and fanciful stories led me to several dead ends. Someone in Bratislava told me about a village in Slovakia where the people were moved because they were dying of cancer caused by fumes from a near-by aluminum factory. I went there to find that they had been moved because the factory wanted to expand and have a new road built straight through the village—hardly a democratic decision, but with the communist command system such things are possible. And it was the factory workers exposed to tar fumes released during the electrolytic process who were getting the cancers, not the villagers. I looked into a report of an alarming infant-mortality rate in a highly polluted East German city. The rate, in fact, turned out to be comparable to those of Western Europe. I listened to frightening tales of malformed babies being born, a theme that came up so often I asked a psychologist in Hungary to explain.

"You've hit on an interesting question," she said. "There could be poisonous chemicals in your drinking water, heavy metals in your vegetables, cancer-forming gases in the air, or radioactivity in your home, but they're all invisible. Fear of the unknown is the problem. Our most deep-seated fears are connected with ill health, death, and the safety of our unborn children. That is why we always hear about cancers and birth defects when people are worried about harmful things in the environment.

cause, forests all over Europe are in trouble.

Nowhere is this more apparent than in Jelenia Góra, a resort town in southwest Poland near the Czechoslovak border, once a German-speaking region. Most of the Germans left when Poland's boundaries were redrawn at the end of World War II. My guide at Jelenia Góra was bilingual and much in demand by Germans returning to the haunts of their childhood. As we drove out of the valley, winding slowly through densely forested hills, he pointed out that many of the trees were losing their needles.

"It's the first sign of ill health," he said. "The needles get fewer and fewer, and eventually the tree gives up and dies." We climbed through the forest, which gave way to irregular treeless spaces covered with scrub and small birch trees and finally opened out into what could have been rolling grasslands were it not for the tree stumps.

"Last year so many trees died that the army was called in to fell them," he said. "I brought an elderly German couple up here, and the old man broke down and cried. He kept saying

Linking a defect or cancer to a single environmental hazard is extraordinarily difficult."

Common sense says it is unhealthy to live in a city with air contaminated with smoke and metal-laden dust, but it is unrealistic to blame the poor health of people living in polluted areas entirely on the fumes and chemicals put out by industry. The effect of overcrowded housing, unhealthy food, inadequate medical facilities, smoking, and alcohol are probably much more harmful. Why was everything being blamed on pollution when it was obvious that better medical care would immediately improve the life expectancy of adults and newborns?

I began to understand when I visited the State Environmental Inspectorate in Halle, East Germany, where I was greeted by their press officer, Manfred Klima.

"Our organization was set up in 1985 to set norms," he said, "and to measure emissions and control them by means of fines. Until recently the results were secret; however, the West Germans applied heavy pressure to have them made public, and now we publish them."

TROUBLE IS IN THE AIR for an unmasked worker in Magdeburg, Germany, who opens bags of asbestos, then feeds them into a hopper to make reinforced-cement water pipes. Prolonged breathing of asbestos multiplies the risk of cancer of the lining of the lung ten times. Compounding the peril: Smoking, epidemic in Eastern Europe, increases an asbestos worker's cancer risk 50-fold. Such exposure to multiple cancer-causing agents hampers experts seeking to isolate the effects of individual pollutants.

He showed me his files of 1987 and 1988 with the words "Secret Confidential" crossed out. "By keeping the local figures secret," he went on, "it was possible to present only selective figures as national totals given out at international conferences. It is also our job to investigate complaints made by members of the public about pollution. We did have a few complaints, but the level of interest and awareness was rather low.

"Around the time of the political changes in the fall of 1989, the number of complaints rose enormously. When the communist regime fell and the Berlin Wall came down, the complaints came down too." He went on to explain how the level then settled to a figure even lower than before the political changes.

In his view the increase in complaints about pollution and health risks during the upheavals was linked to opposition to the communist regime. It was the only means then available to the people. Open opposition was impossible.

"With the coming union of East and West Germany," Klima told me, "people's concerns have turned to matters of money, family, employment, and so on, which are much more important to them than pollution. Actually the true level of awareness of environmental problems in East Germany is very low, and we must try to raise it by education."

Now things began to make sense. To preserve the illusion that everything in the communist paradise was just fine, the true figures were kept secret. Because those in power were quick to stamp out any dissent or opposition, it was extremely difficult for people to make their feelings known without risk of punishment. I remembered Professor Juchnowicz telling me that when all forms of political opposition were banned in Poland during the period of martial law, the Polish Ecology Club was spared. The government considered it acceptable for citizens to complain about pollution but not about the current regime, so with the ecology club as a rallying point, environmental matters became an important focus of anticommunist activity.

I remembered seeing in the lovely Gothic

HELL'S GATEKEEPER, a worker closes an iron hatch atop a coke oven at the Gross Gasserei steel plant in Magdeburg. The wheeled hopper that feeds coal into the oven is obscured by swirling smoke and gases—including ammonia and cancer-causing benzene—rising from the inferno. But a more imminent threat to workers is

a lack of safety measures. One false step off the rail and onto the superheated oven could mean death. Outdated plants like this use technology abandoned in the West, which for decades has striven to limit pollutants that result from making coke, the fuel for blast furnaces.

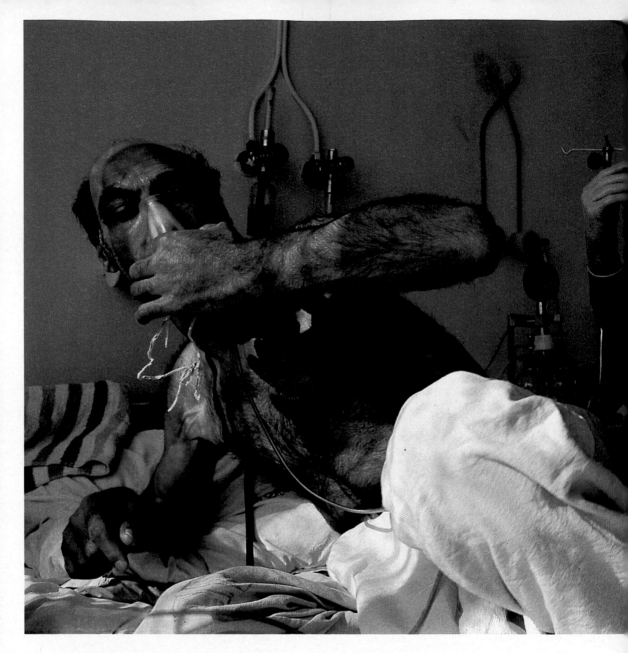

church in Pirna, East Germany, a notice board with the title: "Protecting the Creation." On it were photographs of rubbish dumps, factory chimneys, and other unnatural and ugly things. The message was that humans are part of God's creation and therefore responsible for it. The Protestant Church was, in its own quiet way, acting as a channel for protest against the regime in East Germany, where the ever present secret police made any open opposition extremely difficult. Concern for the environment was a perfect way of registering protest without alarm bells ringing in police headquarters. After all, what could be wrong with people wanting pure water, clean air, and a rubbish-free environment for their children?

As the communist regimes with all their characteristic secrecy and paranoia fell apart, the people who were politically active, mainly intellectuals, did their best to tell the outside world about the poor state of the environment. Air and water pollution and declining life expectancy in Eastern Europe were pointed out as evidence of the unsatisfactory performance of the communist system. In place of the old message "Look how good our statistics are; everything in our communist paradise is wonderful" was the new message: "Look how bad everything is; communist rule is a disaster, please help us."

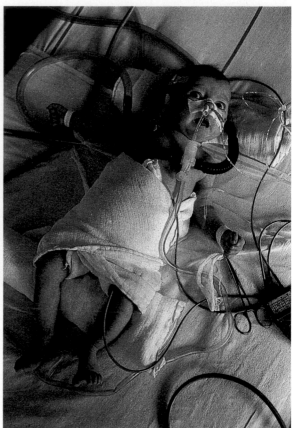

I F ONE REASON for people's wish to exaggerate the horrors of pollution had become clearer, its real effect on the health of the population had not. To get some facts, I braved the cheerless corridors of Prague's Ministry of Health to study statistical maps of Czechoslovakia, looking for the link between pollution and disease. The most polluted area for sulfur dioxide emissions and dust fallout is in the extreme northwest, near the border with Germany. This same area has the highest overall mortality, the highest mortality from cancer, and the lowest life expectancy and is, therefore, also the most unhealthy part of the country. So the link seems to exist, though the effect of poor living conditions and lack of medical facilities is unknown.

The region is blessed with a spectacular rolling landscape studded with wooded hills rising steeply to the mountains. Passing bleak stands of dead conifers, I climbed to a spot overlooking the valley, where many chemical factories and coal-burning industries are strung out between Chomutov, Most, and Teplice. I counted seven major industrial complexes and could see open-pit mines and an odd-looking green lake. Here I met Miloš, a truck driver in his 30s, who had constructed a special aerial at home and was making good money by selling videos illegally recorded from West German

YEARNING TO BREATHE FREELY, many East Europeans become refugees from the air. At Primary School 10 in Most, Czechoslovakia, children practice donning face masks issued by the town council for use on sulfur dioxide alert days.

Shrouded in steam mist (facing page), a Hungarian respiratory patient finds relief from Budapest's polluted air in an "inhalatorium" booth. Some days the smog is so bad that residents of Buda can barely see their companion city, Pest, just across the Danube.

television. I asked him what it was like living in the most polluted and unhealthy part of Czechoslovakia.

He looked vacant, shrugged, and started to tell me his plans to buy a restaurant. When I pressed him, he told me how cool, smoke-laden air trapped between the mountains causes the frequent buildup of smog in the valley. "Sometimes they announce an emergency on the radio," he said. "Old people and children are not supposed to go out, so I keep my two daughters at home away from school. I've had both of them in the hospital with bronchitis. I suppose it must be the bad air," he added, as if these were things in life that just have to be accepted.

But what does this smoke laden with cadmium, fluorides, lead, organic solvents, and other pollutants I had heard about actually do to people? I questioned every specialist I came across to try to find out. The effect of absorbing fairly large quantities, I was told, is well-known. For example, cadmium causes thinning of the bones; fluoride causes thickening of the bones; lead causes anemia and mental retardation in children; and organic solvents have various effects, including dulling of the brain and severe liver damage. The difficulty is in trying to establish the effect of small quantities taken over a long period of time. What, for instance, is the effect on bones if cadmium and fluoride are taken together? The truth is that research is continuing and nobody really knows, though many substances, in particular some chlorinated compounds and heavy metals, seem to make people susceptible to cancer.

In the hope of getting more specific information, I returned to the city of Prague to call on Vladimír Bencko, a tall, dignified doctor internationally known as an environmental health specialist. "Now that people here are smoking more, how is it possible to tell whether their diseases are caused by smoking or pollution?" I asked.

"This is extremely difficult," he said, "but there are effects on health that can be linked to specific pollutants. There was a power station in Slovakia burning coal with a high arsenic content. It was depositing between a half and one ton of arsenic a day onto the countryside for 20 miles around. The first we knew was a report of bees dying out. Then we learned from music teachers of many partly deaf schoolchildren. We investigated the problem and found that children in the area had a high level of arsenic in their hair, blood, and urine, compared with a control group. At the power station we found people were dying from cancer at a younger age than workers at other power stations. People living near the power station have an increased risk of developing skin cancer too. We have also studied exposure to nickel, cobalt, and beryllium. These metals all seem to promote the development of cancers."

I asked him what can be done to remove harmful substances from smoke.

"Electrostatic precipitators can remove 98 percent of particulates," he said, "but the most harmful part, if inhaled, is the remaining 2 percent. To clean that residue, the emissions must be put through a scrubber, which uses a limestone slurry to rinse out the remaining

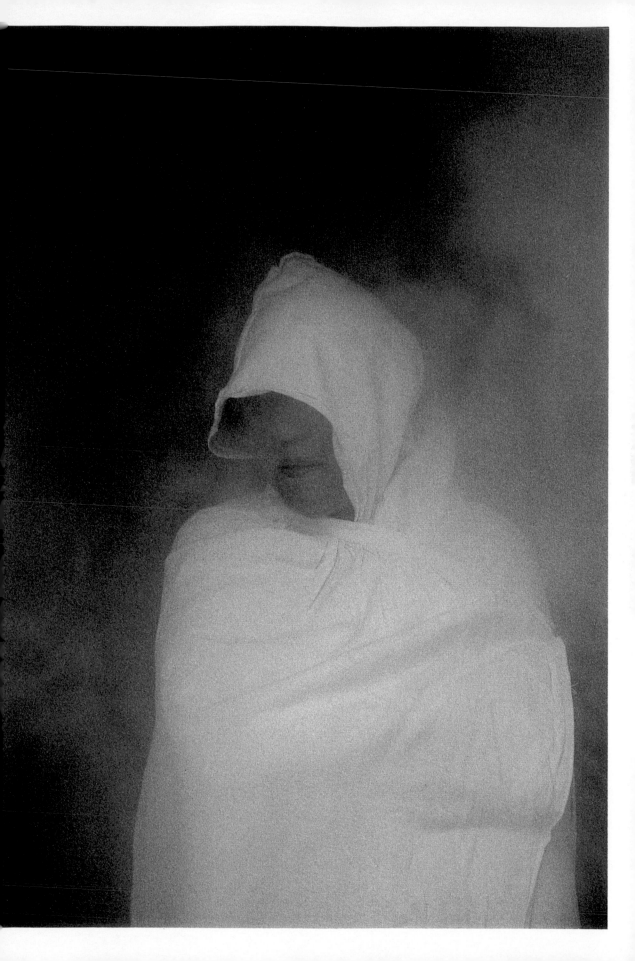

TOPSOIL IS HURLED back to earth by a giant digger after it has been stripped away to reach brown coal in Espenhain, Germany. The coal powers several area plants that produce essential electricity—and tons of sulfur dioxide. Prior to reunification, dirty-burning brown coal provided 73 percent of East Germany's electricity and

heat. That dependency is expected to drop at least one-third by the year 2000. Czechoslovakia, Hungary, Bulgaria, and Romania have historically been less dependent on coal, utilizing hydroelectricity, natural gas, and now nuclear power. In Poland, however, coal use remains high.

substances. But that creates another problem—how to dispose of the toxic rinse water? I believe we must consider very seriously the possibility of expanding nuclear power."

THE PROSPECT of Czechoslovakia turning from coal to nuclear power is hotly debated. I discussed it with Dušan Obernauer and his colleague Igor Pinter, partners in a company making geophysical instruments in Bratislava.

Dušan smiled scornfully: "Ten nuclear power plants were originally planned, but only two are working, one near Trnava. How it came to be built there is typical of the system. Some party official probably looked at a map and said: 'This is an underdeveloped region. This river can be a source of water, so we will place it just here.'

"Nobody asked a geologist for advice because if they had, anyone could have told them that it is situated in the most active earthquake zone in Slovakia, on a classic tectonic fault line. Earthquakes could also be a problem when they fill the dam at Dunakiliti."

The dam, itself highly controversial, is part of a hydroelectric project being built with Austrian finance on the Danube near the Czechoslovak-Hungarian border. It is a gigantic undertaking of the "man conquers nature" variety. Though proposed in the early 1950s, when vast engineering constructions were in fashion, work began only in 1978. It is an odd enterprise because the turbines are on the Danube floodplain (at Gabčíkovo) where there is very little slope to the ground. To achieve sufficient flow for generating electricity, the Danube will be diverted into a concrete canal 15 miles long, with a large artificial lake at Dunakiliti, the upper end of the canal; there the water will be held until it is needed at times of peak electric demand. To regulate the outrush of water, a second dam is needed downstream in Hungary at Nagymaros.

"Absolutely Stalinist," was how Juraj, a student I met in Bratislava, described it. Juraj, a blond and fiery 20-year-old, was a Green, as Europe's environmental activists are known.

"They've already destroyed a major area of the floodplain forest, and there's more to go," he observed. "It's a unique habitat." When we went to see the forest near Dunakiliti, the Danube was in flood. I removed my shoes and socks, rolled up my trousers, and waded through shallow water dappled with leafy shadows. The partly submerged forest was a sublime world of peace and silence broken only by the soft plop of frogs and toads in retreat. "They talk about flood control. . . . This is nature's way," said Juraj with a defiant wave.

In a rented car Juraj and I followed the course of the huge canal to Gabčíkovo. The sun beat down, swallowtail butterflies danced before us, and the dead-flat, empty farmland seemed menaced by the canal's massive banks as they rose above the plain.

"The canal is impervious," Juraj said, "so the water table on the plain will fall. Then they'll have to irrigate—that's just stupid."

At Gabčíkovo, a building site in the middle of the plain, controversy over the project had brought work to a halt. Cranes and compressors lay idle, and the site was deserted except for a few curious sightseers. We clambered around, overawed by the huge scale of the canal, shipping locks, and power plant. Will this ill-conceived scheme ever be put to work, I wondered, and if not, how will the Austrians get their money back?

That evening I was discussing the importance of industrialization in communist thinking with a group of environmentalists when someone pulled some bills out of his pocket. Pointing to a picture of belching smokestacks on the hundred-crown note, he said: "Look at this, our proudest achievement, symbol of the bright future! And how much longer can they go on advertising this disgrace?" he mocked, waving another bank note bearing a picture of the Slovnaft oil refinery.

"In 1972," he continued, "oil appeared in Bratislava's water supply, and for months half the city had no central water." Only then did it become known that oil and oil products were escaping from the Slovnaft refinery. The point is that beneath the soil, extending over 70 miles from here right into Hungary, is a huge basin about a quarter of a mile deep filled with gravel and water. The refinery had for years been leaking oil into the groundwater at the edge of what is perhaps the largest reserve of drinking water in Europe. When the danger was realized, wells were sunk around the refinery in a protective ring and then pumped continuously to try to limit the spread of oil.

"The refinery should never have been built there in the first place," the environmentalist said. "The only thing to do is to close it."

EXHAUSTED FROM PUSHING a rail cart loaded with lead ore, this worker at the IMN Firiza factory near Baia Mare, Romania, sits motionless, head in hands, for long minutes. Factory employees work amid thick dust containing lead, which even in trace amounts is known to damage the brain, kidneys, and red blood cells.

AS I TRAVELED SOUTH AND EAST away from the coal belt along the course of the Danube, water quality overtook air pollution as the most talked about environmental issue.

In Budapest's Institute of Hydrology, Géza Jolánkai, a bearded man who spoke faultless quick-fire English, ran through some of the main problems.

"Nitrates and phosphates coming from fertilizers, human sewage, and pig farms are important concerns of ours," he declared. "They cause long-term contamination of the groundwater and promote the growth of algae in rivers and lakes."

Dr. Jolánkai pushed a multicolored satellite map across the table to me. "Lake Balaton is a major tourist attraction. In recent years, there has been such a serious deterioration in the water quality that we had to do something about it. We have achieved some success by treating sewage and diverting runoff from agriculture, but damage has been done because the sludge on the bottom of the lake will release phosphates for years to come."

Anyone traveling through Hungary will soon notice long, seesaw poles with a rope and bucket on one end, which are used for drawing water. Wells are everywhere; in a large area of the country the water table lies only about ten feet below the surface. To have such easy access to the groundwater supply is convenient, but it means that nitrate fertilizers get there quickly too.

When I visited a strawberry-growing area in the north, I noticed the sign "Not for drinking" on a hand-operated water pump. I asked a woman, whose red head scarf and dark features led me to believe she was a Gypsy, why the sign was there. "I don't know," she said blankly, evidently unable to read. I asked her if she knew that some water was unsafe for infants. "We've never had any trouble," she said. "Everyone in our family always drinks from the wells because piped water stinks of chlorine."

When infants drink contaminated well water, the nitrates prevent their blood from efficiently transporting oxygen. They can turn blue and may even die. Most cases occur in the

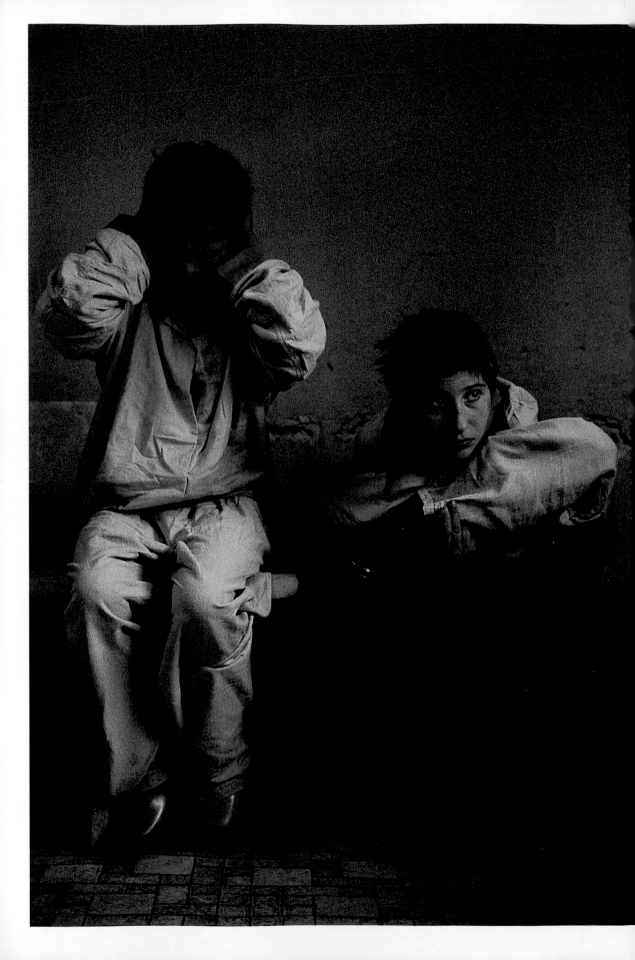

poorest and least educated section of the community. To help offset the problem in Hungary's 800 villages with high-nitrate water, the government provides a free supply of safe drinking water in plastic bags to mothers with small children.

T HE PROBLEM of groundwater contamination is intimately bound up with that of toxic waste. At Budapest's Institute of Hydrology, I saw a map marking the location in 1970 of all the waste dumps in Hungary. Small points dotted the entire country.

"If you added all the dumps in use today, the map would be almost black with dots," I was told. "It would need a different scale to show them properly."

Others at the institute joined in the conversation. "We don't know what to do with all the chemicals produced by modern industry," said one. "We can't even keep track of them. People don't understand that it's no use burying hazardous substances or putting them down old mine shafts. If they are allowed to contaminate the groundwater, they will be sources of micro-pollution for centuries."

"Hazardous wastes," said another expert, "must be accessible and stored where we can keep an eye on them until appropriate technology is developed. The Greens don't like this idea. They oppose every waste dump."

He was right. My Green friend Juraj, for example, had taken me to a waste dump near his home belonging to Bratislava's largest chemical factory. Though it was well thought out and guarded by a resident caretaker, Juraj had been passionately opposed to it and every other waste dump, however well designed. In his opinion, there should be no such thing as toxic waste.

"It's so easy for hazardous chemicals to soak into the soil," said Zoltán Illés, an analytical chemist who did postdoctoral work at Yale and had recently become Hungary's deputy state secretary for the environment. His brown eyes flashed as he spoke of his concern. "We produce five to six million tons of

ABANDONED by their families and by a health-care system already pushed past its limits, two girls share a common fate in the Home for Children with Mental Diseases in Dobromirtsi, Bulgaria (facing page). The girl at right has deformed bones. Institutionalized close to home in Teplice, Czechoslovakia, mentally disabled Martin Höfer (below) is able to visit his family every few weeks. Pollution is not a certain villain in either case, but in both areas pollution-related illnesses strain meager health resources.

hazardous waste a year in this country. We know of more than 2,000 illegal landfills—imagine how many there are that we don't know about."

He told me about a recent discovery. Next to the Kiskunság National Park, which is also a United Nations-designated biosphere reserve, a state farm wanted to make extra money by reprocessing waste from a paint factory in Budapest. When their reprocessing equipment failed and the waste-filled barrels kept coming, they dumped them illegally, 500 actually inside the park.

"These," Illés told me, "were found by chance when their covering of sand was blown away by the wind; 2,000 barrels are still not accounted for."

Out in the countryside I learned that Illés's concerns were well-founded. Visiting the state farm on the Great Hungarian Plain near Kecskemét, where attractive reed-thatched cottages dot the landscape, I attempted to get into the bleak, wire-fenced enclosure where the remaining barrels are stored in the open. A broad-hipped, aproned, middle-aged lady

SWEET SPLASH OF SUCCESS, Hungary's Lake Balaton was heavily polluted by sewage and agricultural runoff until the government launched a massive, continuing cleanup. The popular holiday spot provides at least one happy ending for those trying to reclaim Eastern Europe's shattered environment.

guarding the gate looked me over with distinct lack of enthusiasm. After 20 minutes of hard persuasion, she agreed to let me in. I counted more than 10,000 rusting barrels there, some of them already leaking. It seemed only a matter of time before the whole storage area would become an unmanageable nightmare.

M Y THOUGHTS WERE DIVERTED by a call of nature. I found my way to a little shack with two footprints and a hole in the ground, where I made my personal nitrate contribution to Hungary's groundwater. Lack of sewage treatment is an issue in all the countries I visited.

About half Hungary's inhabitants simply have no sewage system beyond the kind of facilities I had been using, and only a quarter of Budapest's sewage has any form of treatment at all; the rest is just discharged into the Danube. Though rivers have the power to cleanse themselves if they are allowed to tumble naturally over little rapids and gravelly

beds, they are too rarely left alone. Dams are constructed to create reservoirs, water is extracted for irrigation, and the river is confined by embankments to control floods, aid navigation, or allow gravel extraction. Any single dam or project considered by itself might seem a good idea, but the effects of many added together can have far-reaching consequences, as I learned on a visit to the Danube Delta in Romania.

Nicolae Bacalbaşa-Dobrovici, a wiry, weather-beaten professor, has devoted his working life to the Danube fisheries and knows every corner of the delta.

"In the past 25 years," he told me, "man's activities have caused enormous changes. The delta is an incredibly rich habitat for birds, fish, and other wildlife, but it is literally vanishing. When dams interrupt the flow of rivers, their sediment settles, silting up reservoirs instead of building up the delta."

More than 30 dams now trap sediment along the Danube itself, and dozens more block its tributaries. Each diminishes the delta.

According to Bacalbaşa-Dobrovici, the number of fish in the Danube and its delta has dropped disastrously. Flood-control embankments prevent fish from spawning among the submerged plants, and the water is becoming more and more polluted.

"I once saw a 60-mile section of the Danube choked with dead fish," he told me. "A very serious problem is eutrophication — water enrichment with nitrates and phosphates. Only a fraction of fertilizers used in agriculture is assimilated by plants. The rest eventually enters the water system."

In enriched, sediment-free water, algae grow very quickly. In the daytime the algae add oxygen to the water, but at night they use it up. Eventually the oxygen level may fall so low that fish and other aquatic creatures die. And when the algae die, they fall to the bottom and rot, using up all the oxygen. This allows the formation of poisonous hydrogen sulfide, which can kill fish even out in the Black Sea where the river discharges.

"Under Nicolae Ceauşescu an attempt was made to turn 250,000 acres of the delta into farmland," said Bacalbaşa-Dobrovici. "This was economic madness, but it was impossible to say anything against it."

He took me by boat to see Lake Razelm, artificially cut off from the sea to provide fresh water for irrigation and fish culture. The water was bright green, as opaque as pea soup. Passing through a lock into the brackish Lake Sinoe, we suddenly came across a group of fishermen wading up to their armpits and dragging a net through shallow water. As our boat swerved toward them, they looked afraid; one, trying to make himself invisible, turned his back to us.

"They are poaching," said Bacalbaşa-Dobrovici. "Fishing is not allowed here until October, but these are difficult times — we cannot be too hard on them. They probably don't have enough to eat."

We walked along the Black Sea coast and saw the rotting remains of two dolphins. Bacalbaşa-Dobrovici shook his head sadly. "In the past 50 years the number of dolphins in the Black Sea has declined from an estimated million to about 200,000. We *must* improve the water quality, but how will it be possible financially and administratively when the Danube flows through eight countries, and 70 million people live within its drainage area?"

HIS WORDS ECHOED IN MY MIND. I could see that the Danube's decline, like the larger problem of environmental degradation I had witnessed across Eastern Europe, was an international concern. So what exactly is the "environmental catastrophe" of Eastern Europe?

Eastern Europe, it seems to me, was devastated by what I often heard described as the "industrial megalomania" of the 1950s, when communist governments were still trying to force into practice the hundred-year-old theory based on Karl Marx's *Communist Manifesto*. The industrial revolution in the West by this time was also more than a hundred years old, and hard lessons were being learned about pollution, waste, limited resources, and other matters Karl Marx had never considered. The Eastern-bloc rulers, however, were blind to these problems.

A Czechoslovak friend described what it was like in the 1950s. "We had to live under various five-year plans. The bright future lay in industrializing as fast as possible. This way we would exploit all natural resources and gain mastery over nature. The technology was often out of date, but we were after short-term benefits — there was no thought of the future environmental consequences."

Now that the Eastern bloc has opened up, the most outdated, inefficient, and uneconomical factories — often the worst polluters — will simply disappear, and thousands will find themselves out of work. With massive unemployment and backward industry, it will be almost impossible for any government to make the environment a top priority.

Because pollution was used by political activists as a stick to beat the ruling communists and, as Manfred Klima observed, because money and jobs are far more important to the man in the street, the pollution issue will likely fade from the headlines. The sewage and sulfur dioxide, however, will still be there. To achieve the standards we take for granted, huge sums of money will have to be spent. But whose money? How will Eastern Europe's struggling economies pay for these necessary improvements, let alone the clean technologies we are now beginning to expect?

Enormous tasks lie ahead. To tackle them, East and West must join together. But will Eastern Europe's new rulers find the environment as important now as they did when they were in the opposition? * * *

WHERE NIGHT FALLS
ALL DAY LONG

Every sheep is black in Copşa Mică, Romania, where a day-and-night snowfall of carbon black is fed by a nearby plant that produces the substance for making tires. With most local workers employed in factories, a community shepherd goes from home to home at dawn gathering sheep and goats, then leads his flock to the hills, where they graze on carbon-coated grass. The wool will be washed for sale — but only a drastic cleanup will enable Copşa Mică to emerge from its carbon shroud.

A second skin of carbon camouflages a worker awaiting a shower at Copşa Micǎ's Carbosin plant. Even work clothes give no relief from the all-permeating powder — when the worker removed his trousers moments later, he was black from head to toe.

Life in Copşa Micǎ revolves around the plant, part of dictator Nicolae Ceauşescu's drive to drag pastoral Romania into a major industrial role. He was also responsible for draining huge areas of the environmentally delicate Danube Delta, home to one of the world's largest reedbeds, to create more farmland. Although the despot is dead and his policies disgraced, Copşa Micǎ's 7,000 residents cannot dig out from beneath Carbosin's never ending fallout. They depend on the plant — and a nearby lead factory — for their livelihood.

No link has been shown between carbon black and cancer, yet workers at the Carbosin plant still try to protect themselves by coating their insides with milk. At lunch, most will down an entire bottle (above). Carbon black can aggravate bronchitis and asthma. Ironically, residents show less concern for what is probably a greater health risk: high soil levels of lead, zinc, and cadmium from the local lead plant.

The heaviest carbon snowfalls come at night, when the plant gears up. Awakening to a fresh coat, a man sweeps a street sign as distant stacks doom his efforts (below). Still proud Copşa Micăns often hose down their houses to reveal blues and greens painted underneath. Grimy hands frame an old woman's photo of her parents posing by the house she lives in. Her home, now blackened, lies across the Tîrnava Mare River from the factory, backdrop for Gypsy youngsters wading by a campfire (right).

Will Copşa Mică's darkness ever be lifted? Romania's leaders have pledged massive investment in environmental cleanup. Meanwhile, housewives will keep digging through carbon to plant gardens and hanging wash in the dirty breeze. ☐

Secrets of
ANIMAL
NAVIGATION

By MICHAEL E. LONG
NATIONAL GEOGRAPHIC SENIOR WRITER

Photographs by JAMES L. AMOS

UP TO MY HIPS in the dark swirling waters of Idaho's Salmon River this frigid November morning, encased in thick neoprene waders and pelted by an insistent rain, I feel like a fisherman disguised as a snow tire. I am casting flies to entice a silver bullet of a fish, between two and three feet long, called a steelhead because its forehead is gunmetal blue. Though its brain is about the size of a peanut, this Pacific salmon is completing an epic round-trip voyage of several thousand miles entailing wondrous feats of navigation.

Three years ago myriads of yearling steelhead were released in the Salmon's calmer headwaters, hemmed by cottonwoods and firs. When the lengthening days and warmth of spring triggered physiological changes to prepare the fish for life in salt water, they began the long drift some 900 miles downriver toward the Pacific Ocean, there to feed, grow, and roam. One steelhead tagged in Washington's Quinault River was caught by a research vessel 3,210 miles from its home river and more than halfway to Japan.

When the migrating mood strikes again, the fish are suddenly of one purpose—to return

Silhouettes on an October moon, snow geese from Canada's northern Arctic set a course for warmer climes. Scientists focusing on the incredible sensory systems of migratory creatures come up with some surprising answers to that persistent question: How do they navigate?

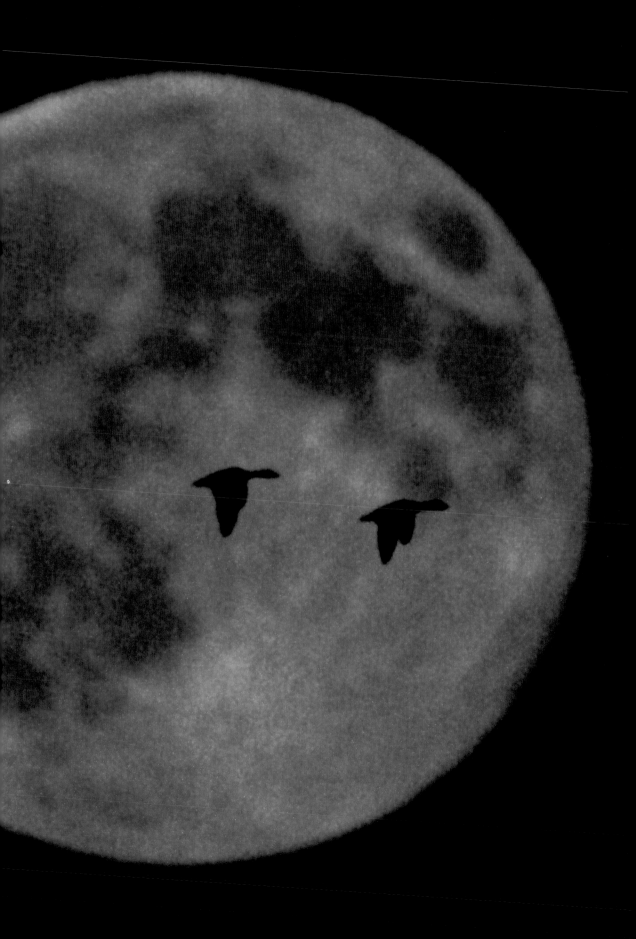

R oused by the warmth of a February sun, monarch butterflies stir from winter bivouacs on fir trees high in central Mexico. In spring the butterflies flutter northward. Several generations are born, breed, and die before the final generation reaches as far as Canada.

When autumn comes, that generation fuels up on flower nectar and flies all the way back to Mexico, despite its having had no direct knowledge of the route or destination. Scientists suspect that genetic programming gives guidance, but how remains one of the mysteries of the monarchs' migration.

Waddlers five, loggerhead turtle hatchlings head for the Atlantic Ocean near Fort Pierce, Florida, when the sand cools at dusk. Researchers have believed that the brighter area toward the sea attracts the hatchlings. New evidence suggests that the turtles actually crawl away from the dark silhouettes of dunes and beach vegetation, a move that puts them on course for the surf line.

Once in the water they swim directly into the waves, the shortest route to deeper water, where the hatchlings may swim for havens in beds of sargassum.

home to spawn. From widely scattered locations they head for the American coast, joining steelhead from Oregon's Deschutes and other rivers in running a gantlet of drift nets, killer whales, sea lions, and seals.

Entering the Columbia River estuary, the fish must escape humans with rods and gill nets and traverse fish ladders—a series of water-filled concrete stairs—at Bonneville and seven other huge hydroelectric dams. Ignoring the mouths of the Deschutes and a score of other tributaries, the Salmon River steelhead enter the Snake and turn left into the Salmon, fighting their way up the raging torrents to the place of their youth.

Now with a rude smash one of them takes my fly and tears downstream with my line arrowing behind. About 80 yards away the steelhead lunges from the river, and I have a freeze-frame picture of a flash of writhing silver that hangs in my mind's eye. My line is limp. The brute has escaped. But I feel privileged to have observed a fish accomplishing this marvel of endurance, survival, and homing accuracy.

Fitted with a transmitter after being taken from a fishing net, a loggerhead turtle designated 04933 enters the ocean off Virginia Beach. Tracking by satellite has revealed the route to and from the species' winter home.

THE STEELHEAD is only one of many creatures whose exploits of navigation daunt the mind. For centuries people have marveled that fish, birds, insects, and other animals find their way over incredible distances to preordained destinations.

"What is most peculiar is that each salmon searches the stream to the place where he was born," wrote Norwegian clergyman Peder Claussøn Friis in 1599. "From a little narrow fjord at Egersund two rivers flow. There is not a bowshot between the river mouths, yet each river has its distinct

salmon, so that one can know the salmon on the one river from that of the other."

Automotive-age scientists studying the little blackpoll warbler's fall migration from Nova Scotia to South America—in which the bird loses half its weight in the four-day-and-night, 2,400-mile flight—calculate a fuel efficiency equal to 720,000 miles a gallon.

Monarch butterflies stream from winter roosts in fir trees on a volcanic plateau in central Mexico to summer in northern latitudes, copulating and laying their eggs atop milkweeds to foster new generations along the way. With the old monarchs gone and all ties to the ancestral site ostensibly cut, an incredible thing happens—butterflies that have never been to Mexico roost there the next winter.

The fabled albatross can teach even a U. S. Navy navigator a thing or two. In 1957 scientists banded 18 Laysan albatrosses on Midway atoll in the Pacific and put them aboard Navy aircraft bound for Japan, the Philippines, the Mariana, Marshall, and Hawaiian Islands, and the state of Washington.

Released at these locations, 14 birds returned to Midway. The albatross from Whidbey Island, Washington, 3,200 miles distant, averaged 317 straight-line miles a day. The bird from the Philippines made its 4,120-mile return in 32 days—or about 130 miles a day. Even more remarkable, some of the birds would have had to fly circuitous routes to avoid strong head winds, leading researchers to conclude that "existing theories of bird navigation do not fully explain their homing behavior."

Indeed. Preoccupied with the fact that

Equipped with the essentials of navigation—symbolized by a map to indicate position and a compass to show direction—a redstart flies northeast. This night migrant sets its course by the stars. Scientists agree that the primary daytime compass for birds is the sun; for bearings on overcast days many researchers propose earth's magnetic field as a guide. Young birds embarking alone on their first migration are apparently programmed with genetic instructions for direction and distance. The map sense of birds and other creatures remains largely unexplained.

Secrets of Animal Navigation

animals migrate, science was slow to approach the mystery of how they do it. Even when the migration pathways of many creatures became well documented in the 1900s, some observers continued to speculate about a mysterious "sixth sense" by which migrants divined routes.

Then, in mid-century, German scientist Gustav Kramer showed that birds use the sun as a compass. Austrian Nobel laureate Karl von Frisch discovered that honeybees take directional cues from polarized light patterns in the sky. American scientist Donald Griffin proved that bats use sound echoes to detect prey. The common thread in these finds was that animals possess sensory capabilities more varied and keener than our own.

Recent researchers, using techniques of the neurosciences, microbiology, and bioacoustics and such fundamentals of physics as electricity and magnetism, are demonstrating that the senses of the creatures of land, sea, and air are incredibly acute. Imagine:

□ A homing pigeon senses changes in altitude as minute as four millimeters. Pigeons also see ultraviolet light and hear extremely low-frequency sound that emanates from wind coursing over ocean surf and mountain ranges thousands of miles distant.

□ A honeybee detects infinitesimal fluctuations of the earth's magnetic field that only the most sensitive magnetometers can measure.

□ A shark recognizes an electric field on the order of five-billionths of a volt per centimeter.

□ Some animals may be able to "see" the earth's magnetic field, a proposition about as staggering as "seeing" the force of gravity.

Scientists are quick to point out, though, that the existence of a sensitivity does not prove it is used for navigation. Melvin Kreithen of the University of Pittsburgh, who discovered the homing pigeon's remarkable sensors, says: "Detection is just the first step." Scientists can observe the behavior of homing pigeons and infer that they use earth's magnetic field as a reference. But then they must ask: "Where is the animal's receptor for this information? Does the animal actually use it to navigate?" Finally, concludes Kreithen, "We must go into the field and prove *how* the sensitivity is used to navigate."

As any Scout knows, a navigator needs a map and a compass. The map helps tell you where you are, and the compass indicates the direction to your destination.

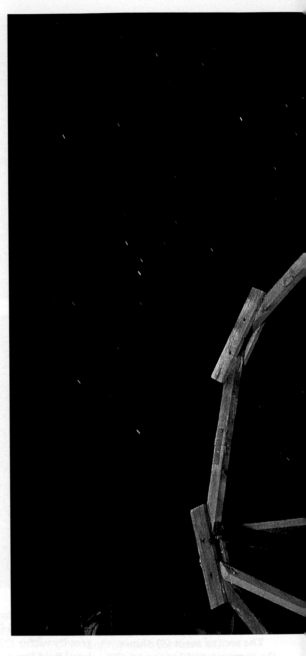

But consider a steelhead in mid-Pacific, a monarch butterfly in Vermont, or an albatross released 4,000 miles from its island. What is its map and compass? What senses does it use? For those juvenile birds that migrate alone the first time, how do they know when they've arrived?

Such feats of navigation have long baffled students of animal behavior. But now scientists who ask such questions are, with ingenuity and dedication, piercing some of the veils of mystery to reveal answers that surprise and, in some cases, amaze.

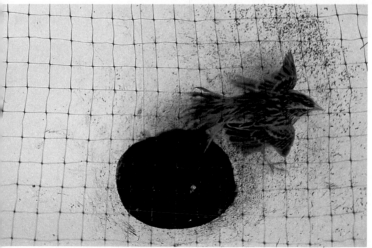

Does a night flyer orient by stars if magnetic cues are missing? Researcher Kenneth P. Able employs an electric coil to cancel the effect of the local magnetic field on Savannah sparrows placed in inverted cones, where they can still see the stars.

The birds maintain their sense of direction despite the loss of magnetic cues. A sparrow (left) hopping from an ink pad at the center of a cone leaves tracks in the appropriate migratory direction.

81

L ET'S OBSERVE THE ANT that sprints. Near Maharès on the Tunisian coast, Rüdiger Wehner, a biologist at the University of Zurich, introduces me to *Cataglyphis bicolor,* a black desert ant no longer than my thumbnail that investigates the palm of my hand and tries to pierce my skin with its mandibles.

When the midmorning sun begins to sear the sands with temperatures that can reach 160°F at ground level, these ants range from their burrows, Wehner explains, searching for the corpses of other insects less heat tolerant than they. When it wants to, this long-legged specimen still trotting around my palm can cover a meter in about one second.

"An ant follows a truly tortuous outbound route as far as 200 meters from home, turning and stopping frequently," says Wehner. "But once it has found prey, it immediately takes up a straight course for home—despite all the zigs and zags outbound."

Since few landmarks dot this landscape, the ant's feat was one of the great puzzles of animal navigation. Wehner demonstrated that the ants use skylight as a compass cue and that their visual systems are especially sensitive to the patterns of polarized light in the sky (page 87).

These patterns are created when rays of sunlight entering earth's atmosphere collide with air molecules and other particles and scatter in all directions. Because most scattering takes place in the blue and ultraviolet wavelengths, we perceive the sky as blue.

The scattering causes polarization—light that was vibrating in many planes now vibrates primarily in one. Distinct patterns of polarization are created: The most intense is always 90 degrees away from the sun.

The eye of the desert ant has a thousand lens elements; a human eye has but one. In their Zurich laboratory Wehner and his colleagues

Airborne over Canadian tundra, an arctic tern will soon embark on a migration that can take it as far as the Antarctic. The tern may include such geographic cues as coastlines and rivers in its navigational repertoire. At Cape May Bird Observatory on the New Jersey coast (facing page), hawk-eyed birders triumphantly spot a migrating peregrine falcon.

revealed that each of the ant's eyes has 80 lenses dedicated to receiving polarized light in the ultraviolet range of the spectrum, each from a different point in the sky. "One lens from 180 degrees, another from 270 degrees, and so on," says Wehner.

He went on to convince his peers that this lens arrangement gives the ant a sort of celestial map keyed to the pattern of polarization. "The ant turns its head when it stops, to enable its eyes to lock into the pattern. This allows the animal to compute the compass heading back to its burrow. It does this constantly. If an ant misses its burrow, it begins a search pattern, a series of loops that usually locates it."

To test the process at Maharès, Wehner built a device that looks like a power mower with a slot for movable glass plates. These enabled him to control the amount and direction of polarized light streaming to an ant beneath. With a smile Wehner recalls the spectacle of "scientists chasing ants that were trying to sprint for home beneath the device. Somebody wrote that we were mowing the desert."

"What we're trying to sort out now is how the ant measures distance, perhaps by keeping track of how many steps it has taken." Its technique of compass direction and distance traveled is actually dead reckoning—short for "deduced" reckoning—practiced by human navigators for centuries. For the ant, however, misreckon and the sun will kill you in less than an hour.

T HE CONCEPT that animals might navigate by earth's magnetic field, first proposed by the Russian naturalist Aleksandr Middendorf in the 1850s, is one of the most persistent and controversial in the history of navigational theory.

"To get an idea of the magnetic field," says

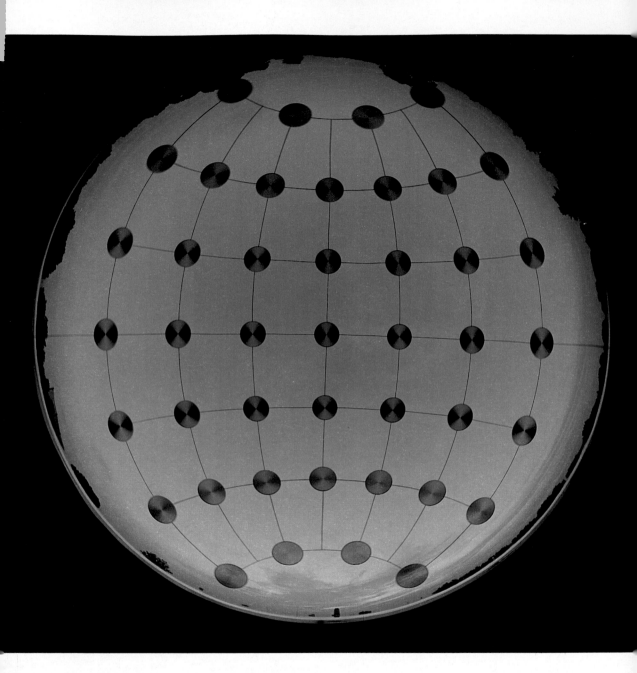

Charles Walcott of Cornell University in Ithaca, New York, "think of a bar magnet stuffed in an orange." The earth is the orange, and the magnet is the fluid iron moving in the earth's core. The field is represented as a pattern, lines of flux extending from one end of the core to the other in oval fashion through the earth, its oceans, and its atmosphere.

The flux lines, horizontal at the geomagnetic equator, intersect the earth's crust at progressively steeper angles—called dip angles—the farther north and south one goes. Where the angle is 90 degrees defines the north and south magnetic poles—to which compass needles point—each hundreds of miles from the geographic poles. Intensity of the field is much greater at the poles than at the Equator.

Theoretically, to an organism that can detect field intensity and dip angles, the field offers navigational information. The problem is that the field is weak at the earth's surface—one-thousandth that at the poles of a child's toy magnet. What creatures could detect it?

On an August day in 1975 Richard Blakemore, a graduate student in microbiology at the University of Massachusetts at Amherst,

84

looked into his microscope and found millions of them. Studying bacteria in mud taken from a pond at Woods Hole, Blakemore had placed some specimens on a microscope slide. He observed a remarkable scene—the bacteria consistently swam toward the north end of the slide. Blakemore joked to his colleagues that he had discovered "north-seeking bacteria."

Puzzled and skeptical, Blakemore covered the microscope to rule out the influence of light on the bacteria, turned it around, and then moved it to another room to try to confuse them. No matter what he did, the tiny horde—15 million bacteria can inhabit a drop of water—congregated in the same orientation.

A magnet was brought close to the glass and rotated. Incredibly, the horde "swerved in unison," he remembers, attracted by one end of the magnet and repelled by the other. Blakemore realized he was seeing something no one else had ever recorded seeing.

Nobel laureate Edward M. Purcell of Harvard suggested an experiment: Remagnetize the bacteria with a short magnetic pulse to see if they orient in the opposite direction. Adrianus Kalmijn, an expert in bioelectricity and magnetism now at the Scripps Institution of Oceanography, helped conduct the experiment. The bacteria reversed their direction. They also made U-turns when magnetic polarity was reversed. Even dead bacteria continued to orient!

When an electron micrograph revealed a tiny chain of dense material inside a bacterium, Richard Frankel at the Massachusetts Institute of Technology identified it as magnetite, or lodestone, the mineral once used in compass needles.

"They are swimming magnets," explains Blakemore, who christened the organism *Aquaspirillum magnetotacticum*. "The magnetite literally torques the bacteria into alignment with the magnetic field." Since the lines of flux dip progressively toward the poles, "the bacteria are oriented where they want to go, down to the mud." For locomotion they use flagella, tiny filaments at each end

that whirl at 300 revolutions a minute.

Richard Blakemore and his colleagues had made the first unequivocal demonstration of an organism orienting to earth's magnetic field, a discovery of such interest that editors of new physics and biology textbooks seldom pass up the opportunity to include a picture of the bacterium. I propose an addition to the

Polarized light patterns offer a compass cue to many insects. Created when sunlight collides with air molecules in the upper atmosphere, polarized light has a structure analogous to light passing through the slats of a venetian blind. To make the patterns visible to humans, Melvin Kreithen (above) of the University of Pittsburgh cleans round detectors—his "windows on the invisible"— embedded in a Plexiglas hemisphere.

As seen by a camera under the hemisphere (facing page), axes of polarization appear in the detectors as fan shapes whose orientations differ according to their relation to the setting sun, at bottom. Honeybees and desert ants employ special cells in their compound eyes to recognize this pattern, which enables them to determine the location of the sun, even if it is obscured.

picture caption to help students remember its marvelous qualities:

 Lacking a good cerebellum,
 Aquaspirillum *uses magnets to tell'im,*
  Which way to yield,
  In the magnetic field,
 But'e needs a flagellum to propel'im.

The limerick points up a fault of the bacterium, at least from a navigational point of view: *Aquaspirillum* is relatively passive. Navigators on the move, such as birds and fish, should have some active means of detecting the field. Kalmijn has been pursuing this for a long time with sharks, stingrays, and skates, a group of fishes known as elasmobranchs.

While dissecting a shark, a 17th-century Italian anatomist named Stefano Lorenzini puzzled over the function of globular structures connected to pores on the animal's head by canals filled with a jellylike substance. Lorenzini first thought he was dealing with glands, but the thickness of the canal walls "makes us suspect that they are intended for another, more hidden function, since nature never acts casually," he pronounced.

Because of their shape, the structures became known as the ampullae of Lorenzini, but their function remained hidden until 1958, when Kalmijn, then a graduate student at the University of Utrecht in the Netherlands, tackled the question as his thesis project.

In Kalmijn's experimental tanks small sharks called dogfish prowled until, galvanized by their encounter with the electric field generated by a flounder hidden under the sand, they lunged into the sand and grabbed the prey. When Kalmijn buried electrodes in the sand that mimicked the field of the flounder, the sharks attacked the electrodes with fantastic accuracy, biting between electrodes just two inches apart.

Kalmijn proved that sharks and other elasmobranchs, using their ampullae of Lorenzini, can detect electric fields as weak as five-billionths of a volt per centimeter—the most sensitive electric-detection apparatus known in the animal world.

To illustrate the shark's capability, Kalmijn offers this: "Plant electrodes 2,000 miles apart on the ocean floor and power them with a 1.5 volt flashlight battery. That is a very weak electric field. But every shark in between those electrodes will know what you're up to."

Kalmijn later put stingrays in a seawater tank and trained them to find food in the eastern part of the tank. Next, he encircled the tank with a wire apparatus called a Helmholtz coil. Sending electric current through the wires enabled him to cancel out the earth's magnetic field and substitute another. When he changed west to east, the stingrays homed to the new magnetic east, no matter what their location was in the tank.

Kalmijn is now engaged in experiments to verify whether an elasmobranch, in this case a leopard shark, actually relies on its electric sense when orienting to earth's magnetic field.

At Bodega Marine Laboratory in California, marine biologist A. Peter Klimley offers another hypothesis: Hammerhead sharks that he studies at a seamount in the Gulf of California seem to cruise along minute geomagnetic gradients—magnetic highways—that originate from deposits of iron in the earth's crust. These are local magnetic fields, as distinguished from earth's main field.

Klimley free dives 90 feet into a school of hammerheads and, with a spear, implants into a shark's back a dart tethered to a transmitter—an exercise the former college swimmer shrugs off as "routine." The shark leaves at dusk to feed and returns in the morning, telemetering its location to a boat in hot pursuit.

"My eureka moment was the first track, when the animal went out 12 miles, turned around, and came back," he says. "Shark tracks are not always straight, but they're very directional. Sharks all seem to go out and back along the same paths. That indicates they are orienting to some simple, fundamental features, which I think are the magnetic gradients in the seafloor."

Klimley rates the shark's ability to detect the tiny gradients as "extraordinary, perhaps so keen that it cannot be measured with any device that we know of."

To prove his hypothesis, Klimley wants to enlarge his research on the geomagnetic properties of the seafloor and also to capture and relocate sharks to see if they seek out areas of strong gradients—the "highways." Fearful of injuring a shark through capture by hook and line, Klimley wants to find a better way.

"People think I'm joking when I say I'm going to lasso a shark." But he has already checked it out by grabbing a cruising hammerhead by the tail—prospective target of the lasso—and hanging on for a ride. "The animal accelerated a bit but did not appear to mind."

IF SOME ANIMALS DO POSSESS a magnetic sense, why not humans? The possibility excites Robin Baker of the University of Manchester in England, a theorist of animal navigation and perhaps the most voluminous writer in the field. To test this, Baker blindfolds students and takes them on a long, circuitous trip away from the university. Then he stops and asks the students to locate it by pointing. Baker concludes that enough students point with sufficient accuracy to suggest that humans have such a magnetic sense. Intriguing as this idea may be, other scientists have not been able to replicate the results of Baker's experiments.

That desert ants use polarized light patterns in the sky for compass information as they forage was revealed by biologist Rüdiger Wehner (top left, at left). Wehner stands on a grid of one-meter-wide squares near Maharès, Tunisia, to chart the movements of a single ant as it maneuvers beneath a trolley pushed by an assistant. Though a shade blocks direct sunlight, the ant takes a bearing from polarized light. Wehner has more recently discovered that the ants use color patterns, including ultraviolet light—invisible to humans—as a secondary compass.

How do ants reckon distance? By counting steps, an experiment suggests. An ant exits its burrow, surrounded by a pentagonal box (left). The insect proceeds to the end of a ten-meter track, where an assistant gives it a morsel and places it in a longer track, where the ant heads for home. Many stopped at about ten meters, looking for the burrow.

Volunteering as an experimental subject during a visit to the university, I was blindfolded and seated up front in Baker's car. I resolved to keep track of the direction and turns—"Most people try that," Baker said—but soon gave up because of his relentless turning (three times around one traffic circle).

After 20 minutes or so, Baker stopped the car and instructed me to point to the university. Then he asked, "Point to north." That startled me. Unfamiliar with Manchester, I had no idea of north on this overcast day even when we started. But I had a feeling and pointed.

Baker told me that I had pointed 15 or 20 degrees to the right of the university and that I had indicated south instead of north—"That's not insignificant," he said. "You were on the same axis—only you picked the wrong pole."

EMERGING from its nest on the beach, a turtle hatchling is confronted with a life-or-death question: Where is the water?

"The conventional hypothesis holds that hatchlings head for the brighter half of their world, the horizon out to sea," says biologist Michael Salmon of Florida Atlantic University at Boca Raton.

Investigating this, Salmon built an arena in the laboratory to simulate the light and dark areas of the beach environment. He tested the responses of green and loggerhead turtle hatchlings to these cues, as well as to the slope of the beach.

"The most important factor is the dark silhouette of vegetation and dunes to landward," says Salmon. "Hatchlings simply crawl away from these objects, a response that directs them toward the ocean." He also found slope to be a secondary cue for greens but not for loggerheads. Brightness came into play

Despite frosted lenses placed over its eyes to deprive it of visual landmarks, a pigeon will still return to the vicinity of its loft. Biologist Klaus Schmidt-Koenig supervises the release of pigeons in a field near Tübingen, Germany (facing page). In pioneer work published in 1958, he first documented the existence of a time-compensated sun compass in homing pigeons.

only when slopes were slight and silhouettes were weak.

There is no explanation for a turtle's navigational prowess in the open sea, including the astounding 2,800-mile round-trip journeys that greens make between Ascension Island and Brazil. Salmon theorizes that they detect wave motion—nearly constant in direction in this belt of trade winds—and may use that in connection with earth's magnetic field to navigate. Another idea is that the animals use their sense of smell, which brings us again to the salmonids.

Like Peder Claussøn Friis, the 16th-century Norwegian clergyman, U. S. scientist Arthur Hasler had a persistent curiosity about homing in salmon, but it took a combination of circumstances to satisfy it.

At the end of World War II, Hasler's proficiency in German led to a job with the U. S. Strategic Bombing Survey in southern Germany. One weekend he finagled a jeep to seek out Karl von Frisch, discoverer of the honeybee compass, in his summer home near St. Gilgen, Austria. Bombs had destroyed the scientist's home and laboratory in Munich.

As von Frisch records in his book, *A Biologist Remembers,* he was anxious when the American jeep drove up. But when Hasler "asked after me and my honeybees," the scientist relaxed. That summer they became fast friends.

Von Frisch told Hasler about his discovery of *Schreckstoff*—fright substance—a chemical emitted when the skin of a minnow is broken by a predator. Scenting it, the other members of the school immediately disperse. That fish could have a keen sense of smell impressed Hasler.

On vacation later in Utah, Hasler led his family to a favorite waterfall of his boyhood. "As we approached, the waterfall was hidden

by a cliff," he recalls. "Suddenly I experienced the wonderful fragrance of mosses and columbines growing near it that I had not smelled since I was a boy. The names of my school chums whom I had not seen for 20 years flashed back. And then it occurred to me: Maybe a salmon does this!"

On Issaquah Creek in Washington State, Hasler and colleague Warren Wisby showed in 1954 that migrating coho salmon whose noses had been plugged with cotton missed a crucial turn in the stream while the other fish did not. Hasler concluded, "Smell is important for salmon to find their way home," and each river has a peculiar odor from its own soil and vegetation.

Responding to other scientists' criticism that the nose stuffing influenced the cohos' behavior, Hasler sought to expose smolts—young fish undergoing physiological changes that prepare them for migration—to a

chemical to see if they would later home to a river containing that chemical.

"I needed something that wasn't toxic or polluting and was stable and available," he says. Hasler also needed something the salmon could detect. One substance, which smelled like horse urine, repelled the fish. He finally settled on morpholine.

Hasler exposed smolting coho in Wisconsin hatcheries to morpholine, then trucked them to Lake Michigan. "They didn't have home rivers to return to," Hasler says, so he simulated these by putting morpholine into several rivers flowing into the lake. "The coho, identified by distinctive fin clips, homed to those rivers by the thousands."

During a lecture trip to Germany, Hasler met Nobel laureate Konrad Lorenz, a specialist in imprinting, the rapid and irreversible learning during a critical period in a creature's early life that determines behavior later on.

A census taker counts migrating salmon at Bonneville Dam on the Columbia River. Lines on the viewing chamber measure fish. Scientists agree that salmonids locate home streams by smell. One view holds that fish imprint on odors from soil and vegetation, while a Norwegian school argues that fish home on pheromones from kin. An experiment at the University of Oslo devised by Pierre-Philippe Morin attempts to discern whether Atlantic salmon smolts exposed only to city water will later react to pheromone-laden water.

Enthusiastic on hearing about the salmon, Lorenz termed their homing behavior a "wonderful example of landscape imprinting."

NOTHER THEORY surfaced in 1968 when British scientist Roy Harden Jones argued that the imprinting of a migrating smolt is not a one-shot occurrence but a sequential process that takes place continuously as the fish moves downstream.

In Norway another biologist was coming to his own conclusions about salmon homing. As a young man, Hans Nordeng fought against crack German troops in the 1940 battle for Narvik. After the war he took a degree in biology, returning to his home near the Salangen River in northern Norway to study the migration of salmon, trout, and char, a fascination since boyhood.

While tagging fish, Nordeng observed that soon after the smolts descended the river, the adult fish would return. Something about the smolts must be triggering the adults' return. That something, Nordeng claims, is an odor distinctive to a genetic stock of salmonids, a

pheromone that the adults recognize innately.

To test his hypothesis, Nordeng took adult char from the Salangen River system and flew the fish 600 miles to a hatchery at Voss in southern Norway, where their progeny were reared. "Thus nobody could say that the progeny had imprinted on the Salangen," explains Nordeng.

Four years later, when the offspring were ready to migrate, Nordeng released them in the Salangen Fjord, near the mouth of another river. His theory predicted the char would nevertheless return to the stream of their kin, a place

they had never been, because they would smell the distinctive pheromone. Leaning across a table at the University of Tromsø, where we were talking, Nordeng said emphatically: "In spite of everything, they found the place, they came back to the stream of their parents."

With salmon aquaculture burgeoning in Europe and North America, Nordeng shares a growing concern among researchers that man may be interfering with the navigational abilities of wild fish. "Along the coast of Norway at least two million hybrid salmon escape from the rearing cages each year. They mingle with

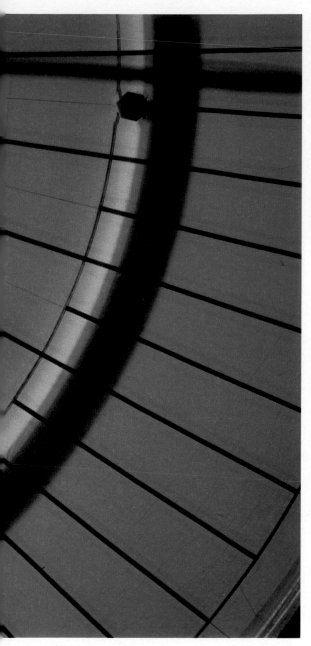

The image: A newt silhouetted on a radial grid between spokes ten degrees apart (left) chooses a heading. The question: Do different colors, or wavelengths of light, affect its magnetic orientation?

The biologist: John Phillips of Indiana University (above). The hypothesis: Animals may sense magnetic fields through specialized photoreceptors in their eyes. They may in some way "see" a magnetic field.

To test this, Phillips implants a miniature electrode in a photoreceptor within the eye of a blowfly (above) to register any change in the electric activity of the receptor when the local magnetic field is varied. A second electrode serves as a reference.

Phillips hopes to answer an elusive question: What is the receptor for magnetism?

the wild salmon and migrate randomly with the wild fish to their home rivers."

The possibility that these hybrid fish are breeding with wild salmon raises the flag of alarm for Nordeng. "We are interfering with their genetic makeup and, therefore, their ability to navigate," he warns. "It will be a catastrophe for the wild salmon, because someday their descendants may not be able to return to their rivers."

These are fighting words in Norway, where the harvest of farmed salmon in 1989 totaled nearly 115,000 metric tons—as against 5,777 tons for the entire world's catch of seagoing Atlantic salmon—and Nordeng has been harshly criticized.

"The genetic component of navigation is a crucial question," says Eric Verspoor, a population geneticist at the Marine Laboratory in Aberdeen, Scotland. The salmonids themselves seem to be giving an answer. Scientists report that wild fish return to natal rivers in much greater proportions than their hatchery-bred cousins.

Sea ranchers, who release hatchery salmon in a river and expect to reap a harvest of returning fish, are often disappointed. "Return rates are all over the place," says Richard Saunders, research scientist at St. Andrews Biological Station, New Brunswick, Canada.

John Bailey of the Atlantic Salmon Federation has been raising and releasing hatchery-stock salmon for 15 years. "Initially the returns were very good; then they fell almost to zero," he says. "Now we are getting about a one percent return. Our experiments with hybridized fish provide pretty good evidence for a genetic component to navigation."

AT MÖGGINGEN, a 14th-century castle in southern Germany, biologist Peter Berthold of the Max Planck Institute is demonstrating that juvenile birds he bred have genetic programs that determine the direction, timing, and distance of migration. Thus the birds get to their destination alone, without the assistance of adults.

Berthold takes me to view "Blackcap City," a complex of 50 aviaries near the castle where he crossbreeds blackcap warblers. "We have several populations of blackcaps in Europe," he explains. "Some don't migrate at all, others fly all the way to central Africa, and still others winter somewhere in between."

Berthold bred blackcaps whose preferred migratory direction was southeast with others who flew southwest. The progeny flew south, showing the "direction to migrate is inherited, as are timing and distance," he says. Berthold even succeeded in turning the offspring of sedentary blackcaps into migrants. He concludes: "Almost everything that is necessary for a bird to know to fly from the breeding grounds to wintering quarters is inherited from the parents. Incredible but true."

Such a capability had been suggested by a ten-year study completed in 1957. Researchers intercepted 11,000 starlings in the Netherlands that were migrating from northeastern Europe to Britain and France. They displaced the birds hundreds of miles to Switzerland. Released, the juveniles continued on the same compass direction and arrived in Spain and southern France. The adults, however, compensated for the displacement and took up a heading for their traditional winter quarters.

The adult starlings met the supreme test of the animal navigator—homing from a place they had never been. Despite being hijacked from the Netherlands to Switzerland, they had a map to show them where they were

and a compass to tell them where to go.

To investigate map and compass questions, investigators have typically turned to the homing pigeon. Now, indulge me for a moment and imagine you are one of these worthy birds, a descendant of wild European rock doves that developed a homing ability to return to their nests to feed their young. After training you are taken to a place where you have never been and released. You orbit a couple of times and take up a compass heading for your home loft. You have homed from significant distances, such as a 600-mile flight from southern

Germany over the Alps to your base in Italy.

You have truly amazing senses that leave humans far behind. You can use the sun as a compass, compensating for its movement with your internal sense of time. On cloudy days you appear to switch to the earth's magnetic field for compass cues. Researchers forgive you for your reluctance to fly at night; they have shown that other birds appear to take their primary headings from star patterns.

From anywhere in the United States, it can be argued, your keen ears hear a volcano erupting in Java or winds swirling around the

Computer imagery plots the electric field generated by a fish native to murky waters, which must sense its environment through fluctuations in the electric current. (A similar fish is silhouetted at bottom in this double exposure.) The fish generates and discharges current fore and aft in circular bulges. Color bands denote zones of equal voltage. When an intruder impinges on its field, the fish detects the resulting change in current through pores in its skin.

Secrets of Animal Navigation

After enticing honeybees to visit a jar containing sugar syrup and honey, biologist Fred C. Dyer brushes them with a telltale pink pigment so they'll be easier to spot in flight. The Michigan State University scientist has discovered that bees returning from foraging take bearings from a sequence of familiar landmarks analogous to visual stepping-stones.

Chowing down at Dyer's feeder, some bees wear numbers the scientist glued on for positive identification. After returning to a swarm, number 50 waggles her body to communicate the direction and distance of the food to other bees, which observe closely. Orientation of the dance relative to the sun gives the course to the food. Duration of the dance tells the distance.

Andes. You have excellent vision, but even when scientists try to confuse you by putting frosted lenses over your eyes at a release site, you still make it to the vicinity of the loft.

Indeed, you even home correctly when researchers transport you to the release site under deep anesthesia or inside a rotating drum. However, magnets placed on your back seem to disrupt your initial orientation under an overcast sky—though you make it home. Interference with your sense of smell also seems to affect your ability to home.

NOW TELL US, worthy bird: Though researchers have come to some agreement on your compass sense, what do you use for a map? At this moment a taut silence descends on laboratories around the world. So quiet one can hear the *coo* of a single pigeon. Not one of all the men and women who have studied your sensory abilities and observed your behavior has been able to answer that question in a manner that convinces a jury of peers.

The principal hypotheses are two—olfactory and magnetic. Although a pigeon's sense of smell is just average compared with other birds, pigeons seem to have a wonderful memory for wind-borne odors, according to Floriano Papi of the Department of Animal Behavior at the University of Pisa in Italy.

Papi explained to me that a pigeon remembers the direction from which particular odors come and somehow organizes these recollections in a cartographic fashion. Thus when a pigeon is released at a new site, it determines its location by an olfactory map and then uses the sun to take up a compass heading for home. But the chemical cues it presumably receives have not been identified, and Papi's hypothesis has been met with skepticism.

Those of the magnetic persuasion argue that the earth's magnetic field, with its varying intensities and dip angles, can give map information to an animal with senses keen enough. But most agree that this would only provide information corresponding to latitude. A navigator also requires longitude.

Wolfgang Wiltschko of the Johann Wolfgang Goethe University in Frankfurt, Germany, has labored tirelessly in magnetic research since his 1965 demonstration, with his mentor, Friedrich Wilhelm Merkel, that European robins use a magnetic compass. But Wiltschko stops short of claiming

that magnetic parameters create a map.

James L. Gould, a biologist at Princeton University, says a bird's "map sense seems likely to retain its status as the most elusive and intriguing mystery in animal behavior."

Do you remember Richard Blakemore's magnetic bacteria? They precipitated an energetic search for magnetite in other creatures. Scientists reported finding it in tuna, salmon, honeybees, pigeons, turtles, and even in humans. Papers were written hypothesizing the use of magnetite to navigate.

Robert C. Beason of the State University of New York at Geneseo has been studying the bobolink. In the fall bobolinks from North America rendezvous on the coast of the Carolinas, gorged to twice their ordinary body weight—fuel for the 1,600-mile flight over the Atlantic to Venezuela. The birds work their way south as far as Argentina. There the male, in molt, acquires the bright black and white colors that earn him his Spanish name, *charlatán*, or trickster.

Beason and a German co-worker, Peter Semm, report that cells in the ophthalmic nerve of the bobolink are sensitive to magnetic field changes—generated by a Helmholtz coil—of as little as 0.5 percent of the earth's main field. They hypothesize that this capability "may be involved in the detection of the magnetic map used for navigation."

Beason plans to remagnetize bobolinks, as Blakemore and Kalmijn remagnetized *Aquaspirillum*. "If the remagnetized birds orient differently from normal birds," he says, "that points to a transducer in the bird that utilizes magnetite, or a similar compound, to convert magnetic information into nervous impulses that are involved in the orientation."

In 1977 Michael J. M. Leask, an Oxford University physicist, published a complex theory with the startling suggestion that a sensory basis for magnetic information may lie in a photoreceptor in an animal's eye. In other words, an animal may "see" a magnetic field. Leask's theory excited John B. Phillips, a biologist now at Indiana University.

After 12 years' work, Phillips believes that he has established a link between the visual system and magnetic field sensitivity in the blowfly and a migratory salamander, the red-spotted newt. But the goal remains. "I haven't yet tapped into the receptor that has actually given up vision to do magnetic reception," he says.

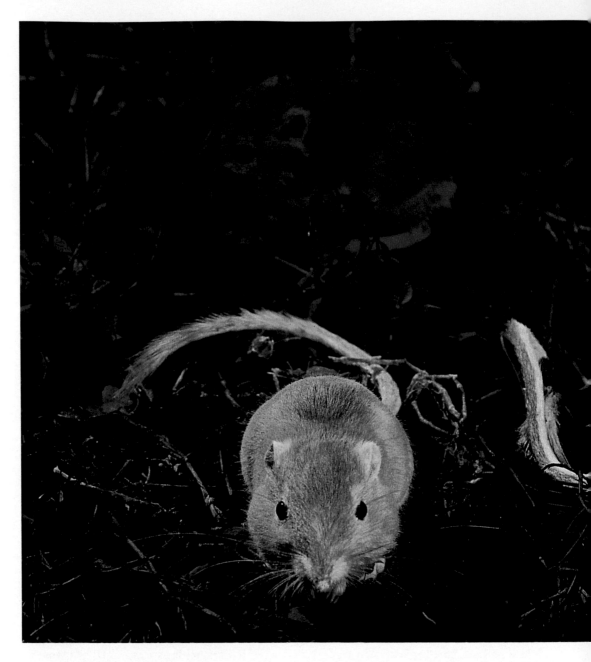

Some observers feel that Beason, Semm, and Phillips are bringing a promising dimension. But Donald Griffin of bat-echolocation fame speaks for many critics of the magnetic school: "There have been some interesting results, and we may very well be at the dawn of a magnetic age, but the experiments have been exceedingly difficult to replicate."

Could animals be using some "factor X" sensory capability not yet recognized?

Answers Melvin Kreithen: "If we are going to understand animal navigation, we must discover a new sensory channel. Existing ones are not sufficient to explain the behavior."

In 1942 Henry L. Yeagley, a Pennsylvania State College physicist, proposed that a homing pigeon could tune into the earth's magnetic field and, simultaneously, sense the effect of the earth's rotation on its flight path—the Coriolis effect, named after the French engineer who described it. Yeagley argued that magnetic and Coriolis information would create a "navigational grid work" akin to lines of latitude and longitude, thus supplying the two coordinates for position finding.

Yeagley's experiments were dismissed by

Dusted with harmless pigments that fluoresce under ultraviolet light, kangaroo rats (left) are loosed to roam Nebraska's Sand Hills at night. Fallen pigment marks their trails (below), enabling biologists at the University of Nebraska State Museum to chart the rats' comings and goings. How they keep their bearings remains one more mystery of animal navigation to be solved another day.

those who thought it farfetched that a pigeon could sense the earth's rotation.

"Though Yeagley didn't really prove his case, history is showing that he was asking the right questions," says Kreithen, who agrees that a pigeon might sense the earth's rotation. "People on a revolving disk detect rotations as slow as one every 2.4 hours. That's just an order of magnitude away from detecting the rotation of the earth. So it's not unreasonable to ask if an animal has that ability."

James Gould comments: "Given the contradictory results we get in pigeon studies, we probably should go out and do Yeagley's experiments again.

"At the turn of the century," Gould continues, "we assumed that animals were color-blind, and it was an incredible shock for some of us to learn that bees had color vision. Later on we discovered that fish could hear, pigeons could see ultraviolet light, and snakes have an infrared sensing apparatus.

"The whole history of animal behavior is the animals taking us by surprise," says Gould. "Why shouldn't they have some surprises for us now?" □

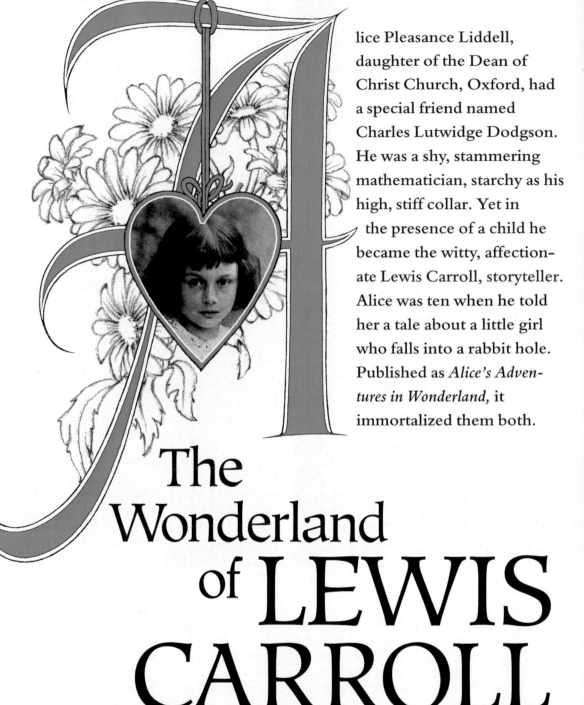

lice Pleasance Liddell, daughter of the Dean of Christ Church, Oxford, had a special friend named Charles Lutwidge Dodgson. He was a shy, stammering mathematician, starchy as his high, stiff collar. Yet in the presence of a child he became the witty, affectionate Lewis Carroll, storyteller. Alice was ten when he told her a tale about a little girl who falls into a rabbit hole. Published as *Alice's Adventures in Wonderland,* it immortalized them both.

The Wonderland of LEWIS CARROLL

By CATHY NEWMAN NATIONAL GEOGRAPHIC SENIOR STAFF
Photographs by SAM ABELL

C L Dodgson

The window in the Christ Church library office where Dodgson worked frames the compass of his adult life: church, college, and, below, the deanery garden where Alice and her sisters played. His photograph of Alice dressed as a beggar

child rests next to an inscribed facsimile of the Alice *manuscript and an album with his portrait. His artistic sense and love of gadgetry merged in his photography; he became the premier Victorian photographer of children.*

AT THE EDGE of an English meadow a rabbit expert flipped through my copy of *Alice's Adventures in Wonderland* and stopped at the picture of the large, white rabbit studying his watch. *"Oryctolagus cuniculus,"* John Sandford, chairman of the British Rabbit Council, pronounced. "An albino. Pink eyes, you know. Absolutely domestic. Can't survive in the wild."

Pointing to a hedgerow, he showed me a rabbit hole, guarded by bramble and nettle.

"Unlike the one Alice fell into, burrows never go straight down," he said. "They run parallel to the surface."

He snapped off a twig from an overhanging tree and dropped it into the hole. It went straight down.

"Strange," he said, and stooped for a closer look.

CHARLES LUTWIDGE DODGSON, the shy Oxford don who wrote *Alice* under the pen name Lewis Carroll, would have been delighted. He reveled in the unexpected. In *Alice* and its sequel, *Through the Looking-Glass,* he celebrated manic absurdity. In his tales, logic spins like a carousel ("If you'll tell me what language 'fiddle-de-dee' is, I'll tell you the French for it!"). Puns teeter on the brink of outrageous (a tree can bark; it says "boughwough"). Words dance with joy ("O frabjous day!").

Even his pen name was a play on words. He transposed Charles Lutwidge, transformed it to Ludovic Carolus, and emerged as Lewis Carroll.

In a moment of pure magic, on a summer day in 1862, he conjured the story of a self-assured young girl who tumbles through a rabbit hole into Wonderland; by turns shrinks and grows; meets the frenetic March Hare, the apoplectic Queen of Hearts, a mad Hatter, and a hookah-smoking Caterpillar; attends a mad tea party; and plays croquet with a flamingo mallet and a hedgehog ball. After the adventure she awakens in a meadow: Surely it was all a dream—or was it?

Dodgson loved children. But one was special, a little girl with haunting eyes named Alice. It was to please her that he created Wonderland and changed the landscape of childhood. What chemistry between a fussy Victorian don and a child could produce such a watershed of delight in English letters?

Dodgson would seem an unlikely choice as creator of any wonderland. Lecturer in mathematics, never married, deeply religious, he left Britain only once, for a tour of the Continent, and spent his time viewing cathedrals.

Yet his imagination danced on the boundary between dreams and waking.

His prolific mind produced learned works like *Euclid and His Modern Rivals;* a masterpiece of nonsensical verse, *The Hunting of the Snark;* poetry in *Phantasmagoria and Other Poems;* a novel about fairies, *Sylvie and Bruno.* He wrote on social issues (opposing vivisection, favoring the education of

"I had sent my heroine straight down a rabbit-hole . . . without the least idea what was to happen afterwards." It was July 4, 1862, when Dodgson rowed Alice and her sisters up the Thames in Oxford and, at their request, told a story. Begged by Alice to write it down, he complied and gave it to her as a gift. Published in 1865, Alice *was first and most famously illustrated by Sir John Tenniel. His White Rabbit (below) finds a counterpart in a modern production by the Parasol Children's Theatre of London. Puppetry was a favorite childhood pastime for Dodgson, eldest son in a family of 13.*

Evening whispers once-upon-a-time stories of moonlight and swans on the stretch of river where Dodgson launched the tale of Alice's Adventures in Wonderland *for three little girls. The poem at right—an epilogue to* Alice's *sequel,* Through the Looking-Glass—*evokes the wistful memory of that day; the lines' initial letters spell out Alice's name.*

women), invented puzzles and word games, and became the foremost Victorian photographer of children.

But nothing ever matched *Alice,* a story that reminds us laughter is the gleam of light in the dark—and the loveliest laugh of all is that of a child.

WENT TO ENGLAND hoping to gain a deeper understanding of the enigmatic Dodgson—and determined also to find a Cheshire cat.

"There are 75,000 cats in Cheshire; what did you have in mind?" Ken Oultram of the Daresbury Lewis Carroll Society inquired.

I didn't mean just any cat. I meant the cat who, in *Alice,* makes one of literature's most amazing exits. He dissolves, tail first: Nothing remains but his luminous grin. My request

A boat, beneath a sunny sky
Lingering onward dreamily
In an evening of July—

Children three that nestle near,
Eager eye and willing ear,
Pleased a simple tale to hear—

Long has paled that sunny sky:
Echoes fade and memories die:
Autumn frosts have slain July.

Still she haunts me, phantomwise.
Alice moving under skies
Never seen by waking eyes.

Children yet, the tale to hear,
Eager eye and willing ear,
Lovingly shall nestle near.

In a Wonderland they lie,
Dreaming as the days go by,
Dreaming as the summers die:

Ever drifting down the stream—
Lingering in the golden gleam—
Life, what is it but a dream?

didn't surprise Oultram, my guide to Dodgson's birthplace.

Daresbury is in Cheshire, a green county abutting industrial Merseyside and Manchester's urban sprawl. Dodgson was born here on January 27, 1832, eldest son in a family of 13. His father was the vicar of Daresbury.

England was poised to begin its greatest age, that of Queen Victoria. It ruled a vast empire abroad, while internally it throbbed with change—the industrial revolution and social reform.

Manchester, with its smoking factories, lay only 20 miles away; it might as well have been 2,000. Daresbury was so secluded, an early Dodgson biographer tells us, that "even the passing of a cart was a matter of great interest to the children."

It's as small a village now as then. You can walk its single street past its handful of redbrick houses faster than you can say "frumious Bandersnatch." The parsonage, a mile or so away, where Dodgson lived as a child, burned years ago. Nothing remains but the rubble of a pasture well, capped to prevent the blackface sheep from falling in.

Oultram picked up a pebble from the rubble and handed it to me. "Dodgson had quite an imagination as a child. He made pets of snails and worms and sent them into imaginary battles."

"But about that Cheshire cat . . . ," I prodded.

"We don't know for sure where he got the idea, but to 'grin like a Cheshire cat' was a common expression in his day." Possibly it originated from a popular Cheshire product of the time: cheeses molded in the shape of a cat.

"Of course, if you want the real animal," Oultram said, "you might check the Cheshire Area Cat Championship . . . except that it's held in Wales!" He grinned, eyes blue as a Siamese.

"You see, there's simply no venue in our county large enough for the show."

The improbability index continued to soar. Fitting, no doubt. Hadn't understanding Dodgson been likened to dissecting a soap bubble?

Still, every so often a clue dropped, a bit of memorabilia carrying the faint perfume of childhood.

In a museum case in Rottingdean, England, there is a set of miniature carpentry tools Dodgson whittled for his sister Elizabeth when he was 14: a toolbox the size of a matchbox, a toothpick-size chisel, mallet, and saw. In them you may glimpse his world of play, which would find form in the Alice books: Dodgson, the child, full of small-scale whimsy and brotherly affection.

He dressed in wig and robe to perform magic for his siblings; he wrote plays for a puppet theater he helped build. As the eldest boy, he nurtured the others, inventing games and stories. It was the beginning of a lifelong love affair with children.

A tail's tale: Dodgson meticulously pasted up the "Mouse's tale" from Alice *to guide his printer. But the perfectionist in him could veer into old-bachelor fussing. He pestered illustrator Tenniel with such advice as "Don't give Alice so much crinoline." Pushed by Dodgson to use a model to draw Alice, Tenniel retaliated, saying he needed a model as much as Dodgson needed a multiplication table.*

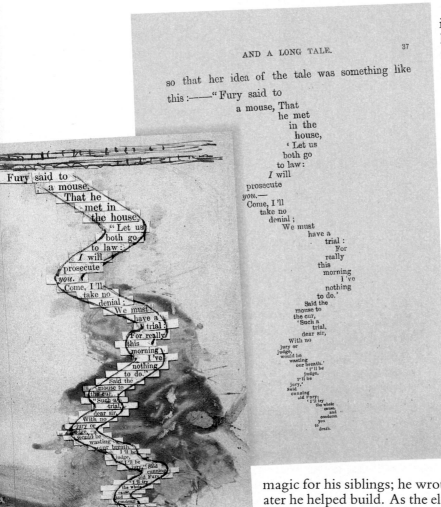

AND A LONG TALE. 37

so that her idea of the tale was something like this :——

When Charles was 11, his father was appointed rector of Croft, Yorkshire. There, in a wind-blasted valley in the remote northern countryside, Charles produced his first works. He edited a series of magazines for a select audience: his family. The magazines, *Mischmash,* the *Rectory Umbrella,* the *Comet,* and others brim with puzzles, parodies, and verse: entertainment for a family isolated in a pastoral landscape.

It was a childhood remembered in happiness, constrained by strict discipline and piety, warmed by laughter and love.

We know little about his mother, other than that she was gentle and, with 11 children, totally preoccupied with raising a family. More influential was his father, Charles: His idol, tutor of his early years, an austere, high churchman who inculcated in his son a rock-solid Christian morality. Dodgson would call his death, in 1868, "the greatest blow that has ever fallen on *my* life."

In a realm somewhere between dream and nightmare, Alice stands among monsters. Dodgson sketched figures for the manuscript version of Alice. *A likeness of Alice Liddell appears in the upper left corner; a possible self-portrait peers out from behind the hip of the standing Alice. Hoping to illustrate the published* Alice *himself, Dodgson consulted art critic John Ruskin. Hire a professional, Ruskin advised.*

"WHAT'S ONE and one and one and one and one and one and one and one and one and one and one?" The White Queen's question in *Looking-Glass* comes to mind as I sit in on a lesson on quadratic equations at Rugby School, among the upper crust of British public—actually private—schools. It is located in the town of Rugby, in England's midsection.

Dodgson was 14 when he arrived, an awkward age exacerbated by his shy, sensitive nature. It was a liability in a place where heartiness was a ticket to popularity. Dodgson was not sports-minded. Rugby, birthplace of its namesake sport, was. He played cricket once and was quickly pulled off the team. He was teased and bullied. There was no privacy, no escape.

The school librarian showed me Dodgson's old dorm building, School House. "In those days," she said, "the butler would lock the boys in at night. He'd slam the heavy door shut and say, 'Good-night, gentlemen.'"

The dorm, barracks-room bare, was a monotony of beige walls, shadeless windows, rows of iron beds. "The boys take pride in the Spartan nature of this," she said. Dodgson, I suspect, wouldn't have.

His letters home were chatty, full of news about academics. He won prizes in mathematics, composition, classics, and divinity. But the letters were silent about his feelings.

Later he wrote: "I cannot

LIBRARY, CHRIST CHURCH

(Continued on page 116)

The Wonderland of Lewis Carroll

Alice's curious adventures

Plunge into this rabbit hole and explore the wonderland created on a summer day in 1862. Passing strange that Cheshire Cat, not to mention the Caterpillar with the suspicious hookah. "Curiouser and curiouser" Alice found them.

Watch the line between real and make-believe dissolve. The Gryphon describes a Victorian schoolroom. The "classical master" teaches Laughing and Grief. The Duchess, like a dotty governess, is fond of finger-wagging moralizing: "If everybody minded their own business, the world would go round a deal faster than it does."

Alice steps straight out of a Victorian England of high-walled gardens, overstuffed furniture, nurseries, nannies, and well-behaved children. Here Britannia rules eternal and ever so proper . . . just behind that cat with the disconcerting grin.

In an age of children genteelly bound by "mustn't" and "shan't," Alice breezes in, slightly naughty, utterly charming. A benchmark in children's literature, *Alice* lacks the molasses of pious rectitude dripping from books of the era.

"Everything's got a moral," says the Duchess, "if only you can find it."

Everything except this book. It is pure fun, written not for money and not for fame, Dodgson said, but for the delight of a child he loved.

Alice also transcends time and place. Translated into more than 50 languages—Arabic to Zulu—depicted by artists from Dali to Disney, it has been concertized, dramatized, and filmed.

And analyzed. It has even been pronounced full of "preponderant oral sadistic trends of cannibalistic character."

One might as well try to gain a toehold on a cloud.

1
It starts with Alice's plunge down a hole in pursuit of a White Rabbit with a watch. "Would the fall *never* come to an end?"

2
Alice lands in a hall lined with doors. On a table, a tiny gold key. The key fits a tiny door, which leads to a small passage. Beyond that: a garden. But Alice can't fit through.

DRINK ME

3
"Drink me," says a bottle. She does and shrinks but leaves the key on the table, out of reach. After a string of frustrations, she cries, and ends up swimming in her own tears with assorted animals. Everyone is wet, so the Mouse recites the driest thing he knows—a treatise on English history.

A trip through the looking-glass

1

On a drowsy afternoon Alice curls up in a chair. She holds her kitten up to the mirror and muses about the world on the other side. "Let's pretend there's a way of getting through," she says.

*I*n the elastic universe of *Through the Looking-Glass* the laws of nature are repealed. A cake is handed round first and sliced up afterwards. To go toward the Red Queen, Alice walks away from her.

Such witty inversion reflects a mind, says scholar Martin Gardner, that "seemed to function best when he was seeing things upside down." Dodgson often amused children by playing music boxes backward and wrote letters beginning "CLD, Uncle loving your," and ending "Nelly dear my."

As *Wonderland* plays off cards, *Looking-Glass*, published in 1871, takes the form of a chess game. Alice progresses from pawn to queen.

It is a progression crowned with the glory of inventive language. Dodgson teases with sleights of tongue and conjures words from air. In the *Looking-Glass* poem "Jabberwocky," he folds two words into one, producing chortle (chuckle, snort) and galumph (gallop, triumphant), words that endure.

"It seems to fill my head with ideas," Alice says of that magnificent jabber, "only I don't exactly know what they are!"

PAINTINGS BY NATIONAL GEOGRAPHIC ARTIST WILLIAM H. BOND
CONSULTANT: EDWARD WAKELING, LEWIS CARROLL SOCIETY OF ENGLAND

13

The dinner is full of the sound and fury of absolute nonsense. The Pudding takes offense at being sliced. Plates fly off the table. "I ca'n't stand this any longer!" Alice says. She grabs and shakes the Red Queen, who dissolves into a kitten.

2

"In another moment Alice was through the glass, and had jumped lightly down into the Looking-glass room." In the room, chess pieces, including the Red Queen and King, stroll about.

3

In a looking-glass garden, she meets various flowers, veritable chatterboxes. Can all flowers talk? she wonders. Only "when there's anybody worth talking to," says the Tiger-lily.

4

Alice and the Red Queen survey the country, marked out like a chessboard. Here, the Red Queen explains, "it takes all the running *you* can do, to keep in the same place." Alice says she wants to be a queen.

12

Alice reaches the eighth square; she's crowned queen. The Red Queen invites the White Queen to Alice's dinner party. This surprises Alice, who knows nothing about any party.

11

The Red Knight and White Knight joust over Alice. The White Knight—a kind but batty fellow who has trouble staying on his horse—wins.

10

"They" are the Lion and the Unicorn, fighting for the crown. A time-out for refreshments is called. The king cautiously sits down between the two.

5

She must start off as a pawn. Her first move lands her in square four, home to Tweedledum and Tweedledee. They recite "The Walrus and the Carpenter," which talks of cabbages and kings and ends with an oyster feast.

6

The Tweedle twins are mirror-image schoolboys, short in stature and temper. Tweedledee gets folded up in his umbrella; the two decide to "fight till six, and then have dinner."

7

The White Queen has turned into a sheep, knitting in a shop. The knitting needles multiply. The sheep hands Alice a pair of needles, which turn into oars. How convenient—they seem to be in a boat. Alice gets knocked overboard.

9

All the king's horses and all the king's men come running. The White King is busy writing in his notebook. A messenger arrives, a bag slung over his shoulder, and shouts, "They're at it again!"

8

Inexplicably back in the shop, Alice asks for an egg. The egg expands. It turns into Humpty Dumpty, who discourses on un-birthdays: There are 364 days "when you might get un-birthday presents. . . . And only *one* for birthday presents." Alice leaves and hears a tremendous crash.

(Continued from page 109) say that I look back upon my life at a Public School with any sensations of pleasure, or that any earthly considerations would induce me to go through my three years again."

After Rugby's ordeal came Oxford, the great old university 55 miles from London. To envision the school as it appeared to Dodgson as a first-year undergraduate in 1851, walk through the lush expanse of Christ Church meadow to the footpath that edges the Thames. Look back. From there Oxford is all spires and towers, and parade columns of plane trees set against a limpid blue sky.

The university shelters 36 colleges under its maternal wing. Balliol is intellectual, so the labels go. Trinity, sporting. And Christ Church, whose dean heads both the college and the cathedral, cannot shed its reputation as a reserve of the privileged. It was to Christ Church that Dodgson followed his father's footsteps.

"The dons smoke you out," explained a classics student

over a bottle of Christ Church port. "Most undergraduates smolder, happy to slide by; they are quickly passed through. But every now and then, one bursts into flames. That one they keep."

Dodgson, they kept. He graduated with a first in mathematics, collected a graduate degree, and was appointed lecturer in mathematics. Except for vacations or short trips to London, he would stay at Christ Church the rest of his life.

"He was the proverbial man who came to dinner," one Carroll hobbyist said. "He stayed and stayed, and for 30 years in the best rooms in Christ Church."

Crack open the door to those rooms. One's a student lounge now—two red couches, a newspaper-stacked table, a fireplace with the cyclopean eye of a television in it. Then, in looking-glass fashion, turn back the clock to when Dodgson lived here. Toys—a mechanical bat, a windup bear—spill

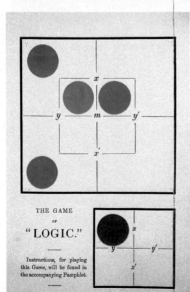

THE GAME
of
"LOGIC."

Instructions, for playing
this Game, will be found in
the accompanying Pamphlet.

from cupboards under the bookcase. Music boxes jostle for room on a table. Drawers bulge with puzzles and costumes.

Surely a child would be present, invited to tea. Nothing gave Dodgson more pleasure than the shy smile of a young friend. Here, in the playground of his rooms, he showed his child friends drawings of fairies; "You can't be sure they don't really exist," he'd say. He'd teach them games he invented: chess in which knights and bishops come alive and discuss the rights of queens, the ownership of castles. And circular billiards, played on a round table with no pockets. His love for inventing games was exceeded only by his joy in playing them.

Remembered one of those child friends: "The truth of the matter is that he had the heart of a child himself, so when he spoke to a child she understood . . . because he spoke her own language."

But the empathy of a shared language did not extend to all the students he taught. One of his undergraduates recalled lectures "dull as ditch water"; another remembered his "dry and perfunctory manner." He was a wildflower that bloomed only in the presence of children.

In Oxford, I was pleased to observe, Dodgsonian whim abounds. Here the Thames is called the Isis (said to be a derivative of its old Roman name), and Christ Church operates on cathedral time. Your watch may say 10 a.m., but the cathedral deems it 10:05.

There is an accompanying logic, a member of the House (as Christ Church is known) insisted. "You see, it takes five minutes for the sun to travel from Greenwich, where world time is measured, to Oxford, so it really *is* 10:05."

Of course. And there was the Oxford dean who when told dogs would no longer be allowed to live at college replied he would call his dog "cats." Dodgson, the mathematician and author of *Symbolic Logic,* understood perfectly.

Although ordained a deacon at Oxford, Dodgson did not go on to take priest's orders. Perhaps his stammer gave him second thoughts, or perhaps he could not totally embrace church doctrine.

For one thing, he loved the theater, an unorthodox passion for a Church of England Victorian. Still, he kept an orthodoxy of his own: He refused to allow illustrations for his books to be drawn on Sunday. He never, ever swore, and once he chastised a cleric for reading the creed too fast.

Gently mocking himself in an ink sketch self-parody (facing page), Dodgson shows "what I look like when I'm lecturing." As lecturer in mathematics at Oxford, he created the Game of "Logic" as a teaching aid.

A student at Rugby, the top-tier English boarding school Dodgson attended, evokes his years on the other side of the lectern. Studious and shy, Dodgson was surely bullied.

He published more than a score of mathematical works. But Wonderland is never far away, says mathematician and Carroll enthusiast Edward Wakeling. "Alice is clearly the work of a mathematician."

(The White Queen's quiz: "Divide a loaf by a knife— what's the answer to that?")

*T*HERE IS A ROOM in Christ Church that breathes the very presence of Charles Lutwidge Dodgson, a room of leather books, cool and dark, except in late morning, when the sun edges in and turns everything to gold.

It is not where he slept or studied but rather the library office, where as sub-librarian he glanced through a window and saw the young daughters of Dean Henry Liddell playing in the garden. They were Edith, Lorina, and Alice—a three-year-old with bangs and thoughtful eyes.

In the Hall of Christ Church, where, Dodgson told a child, he had dined 8,000 times, walls glow with portraits of college notables, including founders Henry VIII and Cardinal Wolsey (right, at center and adjacent right). The high table is reserved for dons, whose after-dinner conversation often drifts into dyspeptic disputes. The Hatter's gestures in a Charles Folkard illustration (below) are mirrored by

Oxford graduates celebrating completed exams (right) with a mad party of their own.

Dodgson, the don, shrank from any connection with Lewis Carroll. He returned mail addressed to Carroll and chided the Bodleian Library for cross-referencing Dodgson, author of An Elementary Treatise on Determinants, with the Carroll from behind the looking-glass.

He cultivated the children. "The three little girls were in the garden most of the time, and we became excellent friends," he wrote in his diary on April 25, 1856. "I mark this day with a white stone." A white stone, adopted after a Roman custom, signified a special day.

Many white-stone days would follow as he photographed the trio, had them over for tea, and told them stories. He charmed them all, but Alice was his favorite. After she married, he confided to her: "I have had scores of child friends since your time: but they have been quite a different thing."

Stand at the gate to Tom Quad, largest and grandest of Oxford's quadrangles. Imagine it's July 4, 1862. The sun has shouldered aside the clouds that dampened the morning. A bright afternoon stretches ahead.

Alice, Lorina, and Edith appear in a burst of giggles,

PUBLISHED BY
EMBERLIN AND SON,
4, MAGDALEN STREET,
OXFORD.

Invented by

Miss Enid Stevens,
13. Canterbury Road,
Oxford.

Ch. Ch. Oxford
Mar. 15. 1891.

My dear Enid,
Please tell your Mother I was
ever so much surprised, and ever so
much pleased, with her letter. And I
hope ever so much that she'll bring you
here to tea, some afternoon when you
happen not to be in a passion: for it
won't do to have screaming children
in College: it would vex the Dean ever
so much. I send you ever so much of
my love. Get a hammer, and knock it
ever so hard, till it comes in two, and
then give Winnie half.
Yours ever so affectionately,
C. L. Dodgson.

Miss Enid Stevens.

PIERPONT MORGAN LIBRARY, NEW YORK.
HOUGHTON 492

Special delivery: Dodgson's letters to children are mini-splendored things of wit and whimsy. Catherine Atkinson, whose family lives in Dodgson's Yorkshire boyhood home, holds a copy of a letter in his "looking-glass" writing. Parrots decorate a diminutive "fairy letter." Dodgson's stamp case bears a vanishing Cheshire Cat.

dressed in white under wide-brimmed hats. It's exactly 126 skips from the huge wooden door of the deanery, where they live, to Dodgson's rooms across the lawn. Their tight-lipped governess Miss Prickett leaves them there.

Dodgson has traded his usual black suit for white flannels and a straw hat. His blue eyes sparkle. He carries a picnic basket.

His friend and fellow don, the Reverend Robinson Duckworth, joins them as they chat their way down to the Isis. At Folly Bridge, Dodgson and Duckworth consult their young crew and choose a rowboat. The party heads upstream, past swans and moorhens nesting under the willows. Laughter floats over the water.

But what is a rowboat expedition without stories? "Tell us a story, please, Mr. Dodgson," the girls ask.

Alice was beginning to get very tired of sitting by her sister on the bank, and of having nothing to do. . . . when a white rabbit with pink eyes ran close by her.

The 30-year-old don pauses. "That's all till next time," he says. "But it *is* next time," they protest. And so he continues. . . .

The tales tumbled out one after another. Dodgson wove them around the children. His heroine was Alice herself. The characters included an Eaglet, named for Edith. A Lory (a parrot) for Lorina. A Duck for his friend Duckworth. And a Dodo for the stammering Do-do-dodgson himself.

His stories that day glowed. Afterward, Alice begged him to write them out. To please a child he loved, he agreed.

TWO AND A HALF YEARS LATER, for Christmas, 1864, Dodgson gave her a dark green leather notebook with the story of *Alice's Adventures Under Ground* written and illustrated by hand.

Prompted by friends, he expanded the tale. In 1865 Macmillan published the now renamed *Alice's Adventures in Wonderland,* with illustrations by Sir John Tenniel. It sold 160,000 copies during Dodgson's lifetime and provided him with such a comfortable income that he asked Christ Church to reduce his salary.

In a book-lined study in her Gloucestershire home, Mary Jean St. Clair, Alice Liddell's granddaughter, recalled: "The manuscript he gave my grandmother sat on a small table in the foyer. We never thought 'treasure, must dust it off.' "

In 1928 Alice sold the manuscript at auction for 15,400 pounds ($75,000 U. S.) to an American collector, who resold it six months later along with other Carroll material for $150,000. In 1946 it was auctioned again.

This time, Librarian of Congress Luther Evans bid with funds contributed by American bibliophiles and bought it for

At an un-concert, as Dodgson might call it, chairs at the Eastbourne bandstand sit attentively empty on a bitter cold evening. Dodgson vacationed here. He invited child friends to visit, took them to concerts and plays, and arranged for their swimming lessons. "He sought constantly to help and divert them," says biographer Morton Cohen. Dodgson sketched his friend Edith Blakemore on the beach.

$50,000. Book dealers, knowing of his plan, had intentionally held down the bidding.

Evans sailed to England in 1948 and returned the slim volume to the British people as the slightest "token of recognition, for the fact that they held off Hitler while we got ready for war." Today it rests in the British Museum, utterly priceless.

Six years after *Wonderland,* Carroll sent Alice *Through the Looking-Glass* into a topsy-turvy world where Humpty Dumpty, Tweedledum, Tweedledee, and the Jabberwock make their appearance and where it takes all the running you can do just to stay in place. Absurdity reigns and nonsense assumes the mantle of truth.

"One *ca'n't* believe impossible things," a baffled Alice says. "I daresay you haven't had much practice," the White Queen chides. "When I was your age, I always did it for half-an-hour a day. Why, sometimes I've believed as many as six impossible things before breakfast."

NOW, GENTLE READER, take pen in hand. We're going to write the famous author a letter. Don't address it to Lewis Carroll. It would be returned unopened. It's Mr. Dodgson, please. (And never ask for an autograph. Remember, he's painfully shy.)

Finished? Post it. You'll surely hear from him soon.

To write to Dodgson practically guaranteed a reply. He was compulsive about letters, writing "wheelbarrows full, almost." He kept a meticulous register of 98,721 he'd sent and received, and that for just the last 37 years of his life.

Happily he could laugh at himself. "I hardly know which is me and which is the inkstand," he wrote. "The confusion in one's *mind* doesn't so much matter—but when it comes to putting bread-and-butter, and orange marmalade, into the *inkstand;* and then dipping pens into *oneself,* and filling *oneself* up with ink, you know, it's horrid!"

Like a phosphorescent dream, a midsummer moon overhangs chalk cliffs near Eastbourne. The walk to Beachy Head, in the distance, was a favorite of Dodgson's. He would set out with a child, stopping for an impromptu story. A child never had a better friend. "He was one of us," one recalled.

When writing to children, his wit bubbled. Victorian children were not to be seen or heard. But Dodgson regarded them as more interesting than adults. He knew never to speak down; to children, one always speaks up.

He would select a cream-colored sheet and in ink, usually violet, begin. . . .

> As to dancing, my dear, I never *dance*, unless I am allowed
> to do it in my own peculiar way. There is no use trying to
> describe it: it has to be seen to be believed. The last house I
> tried it in, the floor broke through. . . . Did you ever see the
> Rhinoceros, and the Hippopotamus, at the Zoological Gar-
> dens, trying to dance a minuet together? It is a touching sight.

Imagine, a letter barely the size of a postage stamp! Or one in reversed writing, to be read with a mirror. In closing, he might send a two-millionth part of a kiss, or a flurry of ten million kisses.

BETWEEN THE TWO FAMOUS BOOKS a shadow fell across Dodgson's life. And it concerned his love of children. "There is not the slightest hint of impropriety in any of his friendships with children," says the preeminent Carrollian scholar Morton Cohen. But was Dodgson in love with Alice Liddell? "Certainly he was," Professor Cohen said. "But it was

Stepping through the looking-glass, in the opening scene illustrated by Tenniel (right), Alice lands in a world where absurdity is the only reality. Sculptor Jeanne Argent (far right, second from right) interpreted the same moment in bronze, using her daughter Anne Carroll, seated, as model.

The sculpture rests in Guildford, not far from the house occupied by Dodgson's unmarried sisters, where he died in 1898 of pneumonia.

a pure, romantic, and distant love." Cohen suggests that Dodgson may have even asked for Alice's hand in marriage. It would have been a hedged query to her parents, such as: "When Alice is older, would you consider me suitable?"

The 20-year age difference was not the issue, Cohen surmises. Social standing was. Alice, of upper-class stock, would be expected to marry well. Mrs. Liddell would never approve a match with a stammering clergyman.

In any case Mrs. Liddell, antennae quivering with maternal vigilance, detected something unusual. In June 1863 it seems she banned Dodgson from the deanery. We may never know why, because the page in Dodgson's diary for that day has been cut out. Four other volumes are missing as well.

Then later there was the matter of the nude photographs. Dodgson photographed children in the nude as well as clothed. A handful of the nude pictures of girls survive.

His motives were aesthetic, he insisted, rooted in "a deep sense of admiration for *form.*" The photography of nude children was typically Victorian, a sidebar to the worship of the purity of little girls. Scrupulously moral, Dodgson always asked the mother's permission and seems always to have had a chaperone on the scene.

Innocent in deed, certainly. Delicate business, nonetheless. In 1880, after a quarter century of interest in photography,

he abruptly stopped taking pictures. Possibly the hobby became too time-consuming. Dodgson was nearing 50. He wanted to focus on "some worthy work in writing."

But Colin Ford, an expert on Dodgson's photography, suggests: "He may have realized he was treading dangerous ground. He was preaching in church, and he felt responsible for the moral welfare of his students. He knew his art was innocent, but he had to be above any reproach."

Best to put the camera away.

DODGSON'S LIFE at Oxford was now one of almost unwavering routine. He shaved with cold water and spent the mornings reading scripture and attending church. He did his writing standing up at a desk and lunched on dry biscuits and sherry. For exercise he walked a brisk ten miles or so. He never wore an overcoat but always a pair of gray gloves.

In the garden of friendship, Dodgson's most cherished bloom was Alice Liddell, here in a photograph he made at Christ Church. At Bodysgallen Hall in Wales a door opens on a garden, and a little girl disappears into a summer day, "lingering in the golden gleam." Of such magic Charles Lutwidge Dodgson pulled a wonderland out of a rabbit hole.

A holiday by the sea was his annual treat. There is nothing like the blinding whiteness, the sharp, salt air of an English seaside resort.

For the last 21 summers of his life he took a train down to the town of Eastbourne on the southeast coast and settled into rented rooms.

Even now, a century later, he would find the familiar: seafront hotels with wedding-cake facades, the promenade filled with strolling families, a passenger boat that puffs past floury chalk cliffs, and children on the shingled beach.

In the golden hour of an afternoon's end, I watched a child of three play on a shore bared by retreating tide. She stamped her foot in the sand to mark it as her own, then, with a laugh like a tiny bell, watched a wave erase her imprimatur.

Dodgson would have been pleased. Eastbourne rang with the high, sweet voices of children. Armed with a bag filled with games to vanquish boredom, he went forth, a knight of the nursery.

Children were a tonic, he said. "They are three-fourths of my life. I cannot understand how anyone could be bored by little children." And with them, he didn't stutter.

And how could any child be bored by Mr. Dodgson? Once when a child walked by, sopping wet from having fallen into the sea, he tore off a bit of blotting paper to ask: "May I offer you this to blot yourself up?"

He cherished their innocence. And they, sensing sincerity, responded in kind.

Perhaps the key to Dodgson's soul can be found in a letter he wrote his dear friend, actress Ellen Terry: "One of the deep secrets of Life . . . [is] that all that is really *worth* the doing, is what we do for *others*."

That was the core of his belief.

Yet his psyche remains elusive. Just when you think you've pinned him down, he's up and gone; there's nothing left but a grin as wide as the Thames.

But wait, there is *something*. A dream of a book. An absurd, delicious joke. A gift of love for a little girl with dark, thoughtful eyes.

In booking passage down the rabbit hole, or to any realm in the geography of the imagination, best to accompany a child. Children know to follow their hearts. We forget.

Charles Lutwidge Dodgson never forgot. In a sense, he never grew up. As he might have said, he preferred growing down.

He died of pneumonia at 65, in the house in Guildford, Surrey, where his unmarried sisters lived. The doctor, descending the staircase to break the news, gently said: "How wonderfully young your brother looks!"

IRRESISTIBLE MIDNIGHT SNACK, the luscious fruit of a saguaro cactus wafts its aroma through the chilly night air of Mexico's Sonoran Desert. On a whir of paper-thin wings, a lesser long-nosed bat, shown nearly life-size, grabs a mouthful, reaffirming an important relationship. Eating in flight, the bat repays the saguaro by dispersing its seeds.

Making such observations—the essence of bat research—takes great patience. There were nights I thought I'd freeze to death, staring through night-vision scopes with my colleague, Theodore H. Fleming of the University of Miami. Our studies were conducted in the spring of 1989 and 1990 at Bahía Kino on Mexico's west coast. There, under controlled conditions, I made photographs to show the link between these airborne mammals and three species of cactus.

In spring, as lesser long-nosed bats begin their northward migration from southern Mexico, they feed on nectar from flowers of the saguaro, organ-pipe, and cardon cactuses, thereby transferring pollen from plant to plant and enabling them to reproduce. As more bats return in June, they perform another service by eating cactus fruits and dispersing seeds.

Each cactus has evolved a flowering strategy that takes best advantage of the bats' migratory and feeding habits. This species of bat is thus essential to some of the desert's most important plants, and the fact that the bats' numbers appear to be declining raises concern for the entire ecosystem.

BATS
THE CACTUS CONNECTION

Text and photographs by
MERLIN D. TUTTLE

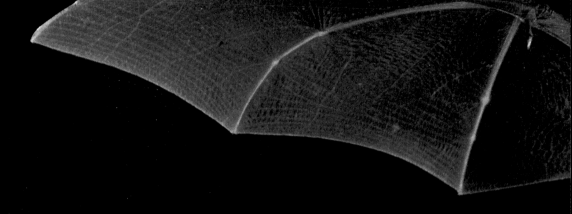

L IKE A KEY AND A LOCK the head of a lesser long-nosed bat and a
saguaro flower are closely matched. A revealing series arrests
one bat in mid-approach (below). Up to its ears, the ravenous
forager laps up nectar in the bottom of a flower (right). When the
bat withdraws (far right), its head is covered with pollen, which is
transferred to other flowers as the bat makes its rounds.

The saguaro is not totally bat dependent. Unlike the flowers of
the organ-pipe and cardon cactuses, which open at dusk and close
by midmorning, the blossoms of the saguaro open well after dark
and remain open through much of the following day, attracting
additional pollinators such as birds and bees.

DESERT DESIGN: A WEB OF LIFE

Cardon cactus flowers, left background, open at dusk to attract bats. A *pack rat* feeds on ripe fruit. *Elf owls* nest in a vacant woodpecker hole. *Saguaro flowers* open later at night, as bats feed, and remain open until the following afternoon. The head of a *white-winged dove*

carries pollen from plant to plant. **Organ-pipe cactus,** growing just behind the saguaro, opens its flowers at night, mostly in June. Side by side, a **saguaro** and a **cardon,** right background, show the different heights at which each branches. A **red-tailed hawk** with chicks nests in the saguaro. Perched gingerly atop spines, an **antelope ground squirrel** feeds on saguaro fruit. The column of a cardon furnishes a nest hole to a **gila woodpecker** with a pair of young.

URVIVAL PRESSURE RISES in June, when the Sonoran Desert is at its driest and interdependence, always a necessity, becomes critical. A relationship that benefits both parties—like the nocturnal meeting of bat and cactus—is an example of mutualism. Many other animals, including day creatures, rely on the cactuses for food and shelter.

By night, at far left, flowers of the cardon and organ-pipe cactuses—the species most dependent on bats for pollination—open wide. Small mammals and birds seek fruit or shelter among the spines or in nest holes carved out by woodpeckers. Towering as high as 50 feet, saguaro cactuses offer a nectar feast at night and for much of the day. Bats, birds, and insects gain precious moisture as well as energy from the sugary liquid. Mammals such as antelope ground squirrels, foxes, and ringtails also feed on fruits.

A RESEARCH PROJECT SUPPORTED IN PART BY YOUR SOCIETY

Human interference can disrupt these natural associations. Our studies at Bahía Kino showed that cardon and organ-pipe cactuses are not producing as much fruit as they could. The shortfall is apparently due to the displacement of many bats, chased from their caves by villagers, to the offshore island of Tiburón (map, below). While some bats do make the nightly round-trip to visit mainland cactuses, many flowers go unvisited. The long-term effects are not yet clear. There is concern that some of these plants, which live for centuries, may be yielding fewer seeds than necessary to ensure their replacement.

PAINTING BY JOHN D. DAWSON

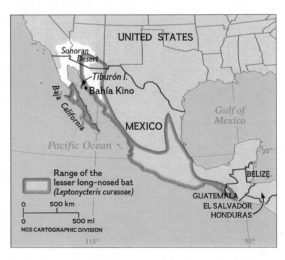

UNITED STATES

Sonoran Desert

Tiburón I.

Bahía Kino

Baja California

MEXICO

Gulf of Mexico

Pacific Ocean

BELIZE

GUATEMALA
EL SALVADOR
HONDURAS

Range of the
lesser long-nosed bat
(Leptonycteris curasoae)

0   500 km
0   500 mi
NGS CARTOGRAPHIC DIVISION

110°   90°

137

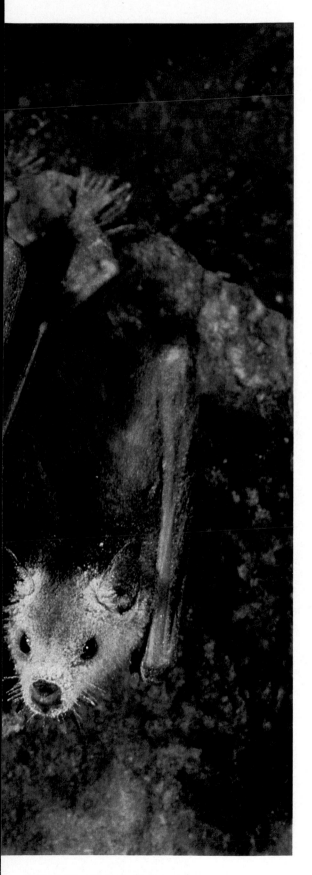

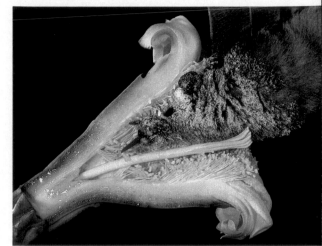

PLASTERED WITH POLLEN, a bat quartet
roosts in a cave after a fine night of feeding. Bats lick pollen from their faces
after eating, making the most of its protein. A
cutaway view (above) reveals a near-perfect fit
between a bat's probing head and the flower of
a cardon cactus, a species with extraordinary
sexual secrets.

Like most flowering plants, many cardons
are bisexual, producing blossoms with both
pollen—the male function—and female ovules.
But as recently discovered by Ted Fleming,
some cardon plants are all-male, producing
flowers with pollen but no ovules, while others
are all-female, with ovules but no pollen. The
male and female plants vie with bisexual cardons for reproductive dominance—a very
unusual form of competition.

The cactus needs all its options to ensure
long-term survival, and the bats help to maintain those options by pollinating the separate
sexes. If there were no bats, the bisexual plants
would probably prevail, because they can self-
fertilize. The males and females would likely
die out, reducing the plant's adaptability in a
harsh and ever changing environment.

OPEN FOR BUSINESS, an organ-pipe fruit draws a hungry customer in June. The organ-pipe's ripe fruits allow late migrating bats to fuel up during midsummer, when other food is scarce.

In the southwestern United States the bats supplement their diet of cactus nectar with that of the agave plant. As these bats migrate back into Mexico in the fall, they follow a trail of agave species that, like the cactuses, flower in rhythm with the bats' itinerary.

While agaves supply nectar to bats, they also yield spirits like tequila to moonshiners, who are seriously depleting agaves in some locales. This increases pressure on lesser long-nosed bats, which have been classified as endangered in the U. S. since 1988. In Mexico people often mistake them for vampire bats and burn their roosting caves. Perhaps now the sight of a cactus in bloom will recall the vital connection with lesser long-nosed bats, and the need for their protection. ☐

Merlin D. Tuttle is a professor in the Department of Wildlife and Fisheries Sciences at Texas A&M University and executive director of Bat Conservation International, organized to protect and preserve bat populations worldwide. For information write Bat Conservation International, Inc., P.O. Box 162603, Austin, Texas 78716.

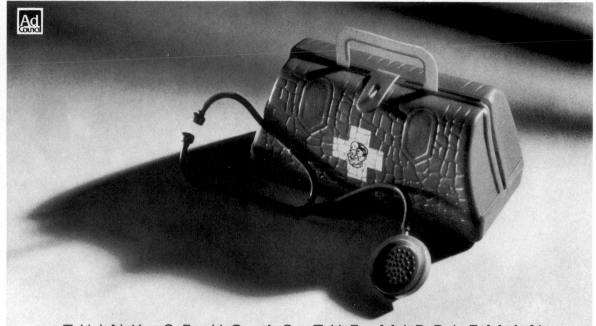

THINK OF US AS THE MIDDLEMAN

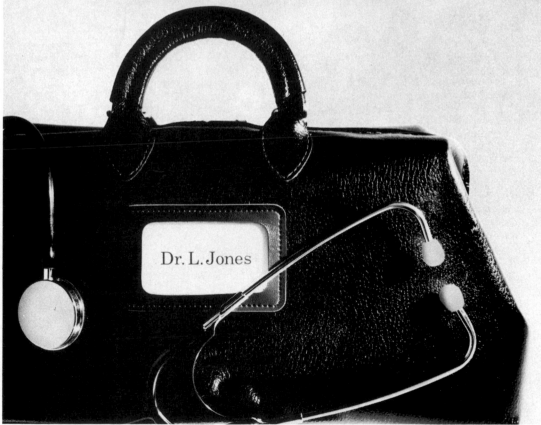

Dr. L. Jones

Earth Almanac

DICK SCHMIDT, THE SACRAMENTO BEE

Dealing With Drought the California Way

These days Californians know how a fish out of water feels, like this one in a bone-dry Santa Clara County reservoir. In the grip of a five-year drought some cities brace to reduce water consumption 50 percent below 1986 levels.

Innovative ideas, however, are flowing. Silicon Valley firms use infrared imaging and computer modeling to find ways to reduce their landscape irrigation by as much as 40 percent. In Santa Barbara, officials offer rebates to people who exchange water-guzzling toilets for low-flush, water-conserving models. Old porcelain rejects piling up in landfills have been crushed into chips and incorporated into a material called "potty-crete," used in road construction and repair.

At Los Angeles International Airport saving both fuel and water are important. There airlines had washed their planes frequently to reduce drag and thus conserve fuel. Now most planes are washed in other states. For automobiles, commercial washes are encouraged because much of the water is reused, unlike in a driveway car wash.

But diaper services create a dilemma for environmentally conscious Californians. The services are having trouble reducing water consumption because so many parents reject disposable diapers in favor of cloth, creating a staggering volume of laundry.

DAVID DARE PARKER, AUSCAPE

New Horde of Tougher Rabbits Plagues Australia

They have been eating their way across Australia since 1859, when 13 wild rabbits were turned loose to breed for hunters. By the 1940s the rabbit population had exploded to more than 600 million, devouring sheep and cattle pastures. Then myxomatosis, an introduced disease, nearly wiped out the rabbits.

Now they're back. Three wet years have produced abundant vegetation to feed the pests, more than 200 million strong and increasing in New South Wales, Victoria, and South Australia, where youngsters in Cook display part of the problem (left). The new rabbit generations are more resistant to myxomatosis. Damage to grazing land has reached about 75 million dollars a year.

In an ironic economic twist, rabbits are sometimes worth more than sheep. With high demand for rabbit meat, hunters sell each animal for a dollar apiece, while sheep fetch as little as 20 cents each because of slumping wool prices. As scientists try to make the myxoma virus more potent, farmers attack with any means at hand—guns, dogs, poison, and dynamite. On one farm 60,000 rabbits were eradicated in a month.

SIGOURNEY

JOZI

Dear Friend:

It's been more than two years since I was in Rwanda filming "Gorillas in the Mist."

A day does not go by without my thinking of my friends, the mountain gorillas, and wondering how they are.

I think of Maggie, the mischievous young female who was such a ham for the cameras. And I thought I was an actress!

I think of Jozi, a delicate little female who used to croon sweetly to herself as she munched on wild celery.

I think of the Karisoke Research Center and all the hard working scientists who happily endure months of cold, wet weather and bad food in order to study the gorillas. I envy them.

I think of Dian's cabin which has sadly fallen into disrepair.

A lot has happened in the last two years. The film has come out and been a big success world wide. The video is doing very well. More and more people come up to me to ask me what they can do to help save the gorillas. Children and adults alike are touched by this story.

What can you do?

A lot.

We need funds to continue the anti-poaching patrols — that's essential — and the veterinarian in residence program. We also must continue the research program.

In the last two years, the gorillas have been hit hard.

My dear friend Jozi caught her hand in a poacher's snare in 1988. In typical gorilla fashion, she hid her injury from human observers. When it was finally discovered, there was nothing that veterinarian Barkley Hastings could do. Jozi died.

I think of Jozi daily, I think of all the children she would have had and what a loving mother she would have been.

I think . . . perhaps if we could have afforded one more anti-poaching patrol, would that have saved her?

We desperately need your support if we are to maintain the strides we've made. The outpouring of concern alone will not keep the gorillas alive.

What will?

Anti-poaching patrols will.

The continuation of the veterinary program will.

We hope also to rebuild Dian's cabin so that it may be used as a working library and resource center for the researchers at Karisoke.

It would also be a memorial for Dian, who spent 18 years of her life there before she was killed.

I ask you to contribute generously to our cause.

My gorilla friend Maggie gave birth in 1989 to a bouncing male infant named Sanuurra or, in English, "Rainy Weather."

Please help me give Maggie and her son a fighting chance. Protect them with rangers and with medical supervision. Don't let our film end up an unwitting memorial to an extinct species.

Please give what you can. We are making a difference between life and death there. Give us your support.

Won't you join me in making a special donation for our very important needs?

Yours in saving the gorillas,

Sigourney Weaver

Sigourney Weaver

The Digit Fund
45 Inverness Drive East
Englewood, CO 80112-5480 USA
Phone: (303) 790-2345

Earth Almanac

Stranded Whale Warmed by Tailor-made Wet Suit

"Whales and dolphins seem to bring out the best in people," says Laurel Canty of the Dolphin Research Center in the Florida Keys. Such was the case last fall when a pygmy sperm whale became stranded off Lignumvitae Key. Caring for the victim at a holding facility, the center's staff dreamed up a novel survival tool—a whale wet suit.

The whale, a female, was underweight and shivering. "We were anticipating a cold front," Canty adds. A wet suit would add warmth. The whale's measurements were sent to an Orlando wet-suit company, which quickly made a yellow neoprene jacket with holes for the fins.

Snug in her suit, the whale lasted eight weeks before losing her battle for survival. Perhaps in the future other rescued marine mammals will benefit from such innovative and tender loving care.

LAUREL CANTY, DOLPHIN RESEARCH CENTER

Cooking With the Sun: a New Ray of Hope

Build a simple glass-topped box. Place it in the sun. Bake dinner and serve—sparing the community's wood supply. That environmental recipe has been known since the 1950s, when solar ovens were offered to the world's rural poor in hopes of reducing their dependency on wood for fuel. But the idea never really caught on.

Today two billion people burn the earth's dwindling supply of wood to make a meal, and half the annual wood harvest goes up in cooking smoke. William F. Lankford, a physicist at George Mason University in Fairfax, Virginia, thinks he knows the ingredient missing from the original solar recipe—community involvement.

"This is not just an engineering project. It involves the interaction of human beings," says Lankford. Since 1988 he has held oven workshops and demonstrations in five Central American nations, including Costa Rica (left). Participants have built about 250 solar ovens using local materials, and many bake their main meal in the ovens.

Past efforts failed, Lankford believes, because previous ovens were too sophisticated, donated from afar to poor communities with no local collaboration. "People need to contribute their own time and labor, to make a personal investment," he says.

In basic design a small glass-topped box of wood or cardboard uses a reflective, foil-covered lid to collect more of the sun's rays. Black cooking pots rest on a black metal floor to absorb heat. Temperatures can reach 360°F, but meals may take two to four hours to cook. "People are a lot more patient in Latin America," Lankford adds.

WILLIAM F. LANKFORD

Tiny Marine Hijacker Nabs Poisonous Protector

No creature had ever been known to capture another that is armed with chemical defenses and carry it around for protection. Now biologists James B. McClintock and John Janssen have witnessed hundreds of such abductions beneath Antarctica's sea ice.

The bizarre kidnappings involve two invertebrates—a quarter-inch-long amphipod and its smaller quarry, a sea butterfly. The amphipod lacks defenses against hungry fish and captures sea butterflies, which contain chemicals that fish despise. "An amphipod zips up to a sea butterfly like an F-15 and slings it up on

PHIL OSHEL; AMPHIPOD, *HYPERIELLA DILATATA*; SEA BUTTERFLY, *CLIONE LIMACINA*.

its back," says McClintock. Wings retracted, the captive is held for days (above). Some amphipods free hostages and capture new ones.

The amphipods gain safety, but carrying passengers may slow their feeding. Sea butterflies, although prevented from feeding at all, seem none the worse for wear.

On Assignment

Noted war photographer JAMES NACHTWEY turns to man's violence against nature for the article about East European pollution in this issue. Crisscrossing the region for five months, Jim graphically recorded the toll in Copşa Mică, Romania, where a factory that makes carbon black for tires coats everything with soot—including photographers.

"Just sitting still leaves you covered in black," says Jim, who posed with workers at the plant (right). "Even the eyepiece of my camera blackened my eye with soot, as if a practical joker had inked it up."

East Europeans react to their plight with what Jim calls "the shrug." He explains: "It's a uniquely expressive, full-bodied shrug that declares, 'What can we do?'"

Jim taught himself photography at age 24, pursued it as "the only real job I've ever had," and has since become the only four-time Magazine Photographer of the Year. He's also earned the Overseas Press Club's Robert Capa Gold Medal for "exceptional courage and enterprise" three times. Eight years of battlefield images are featured in his book *Deeds of War*. Jim's previous GEOGRAPHIC assignments include stories on Guatemala and Nicaragua.

The battle over western water engaged author JIM CARRIER (bottom, front), who took a much needed break by leading fellow river runners down rapids of the Little Colorado. This relatively untouched tributary stands in sharp contrast to what Carrier, a native New Yorker on his first GEOGRAPHIC assignment, found along the greater Colorado.

"In the East you don't have to think about water much. It's just there. It was startling and somewhat sad to come West and find rivers drained out of their riverbeds."

A journalist for 25 years, Carrier has spent the past six as the *Denver Post*'s "Rocky Mountain Ranger," roaming the West and reporting on such diverse topics as racism in Idaho and murder in New Mexico.

PHOTOGRAPH BY JIM RICHARDSON

NATIONAL GEOGRAPHIC (ISSN 0027-9358) IS PUBLISHED MONTHLY BY THE NATIONAL GEOGRAPHIC SOCIETY, 17TH AND M STS. N.W., WASHINGTON, D. C. 20036. $21.00 A YEAR, $2.65 A COPY. SECOND-CLASS POSTAGE PAID AT WASHINGTON, D. C., AND ELSEWHERE. POSTMASTER: SEND ADDRESS CHANGES TO NATIONAL GEOGRAPHIC, P.O. BOX 2174, WASHINGTON, D. C. 20013.

Photo taken in Grindelwald, Switzerland, by Doris Muir, Shrewsbury, Pa.

No print film gives you truer, more accurate color. Why trust your memories to anything less?

Kodak
Official Sponsor
of the 1992
Olympic Games

Show Your True Colors.™